Envision It! | Visual Skills Handbook

Cause and Effect

Main Idea and Details

Literary Elements

Cause and Effect

Cause

Effect

Main Idea and Details

Main Idea

Details

Literary Elements

Characters

BROTHER

MOMMY

DADDY

SISTER

Setting

Plot

Beginning

Middle

End

Envision It! | Visual Strategies Handbook

Background Knowledge

Let's Think About Reading!

- What do I already know?
- What does this remind me of?

Important Ideas

This is important information.

GIANT PANDA

Let's **Think** About **Reading!**

- What is important to know?

Inferring

Let's Think About Reading!

- What do I already know?
- How does this help me understand what happened?

Monitor and Clarify

I'm confused.

Fix-Up Kit

Read this part again!

Now I get it!

Let's Think About Reading!

- What does not make sense?
- How can I fix it?

Predict and Set Purpose

Let's Think About Reading!

- What do I already know?
- What do I think will happen?
- What is my purpose for reading?

Questioning

Why is it cracked?

Let's Think About Reading!

- What questions do I have about what I am reading?

Story Structure

Beginning

Middle

End

Let's Think About Reading!

- What happens in the beginning?
- What happens in the middle?
- What happens in the end?

EI·14

Summarize

The dog knocked over the table.

Let's Think About Reading!

- What happens in the story?
- What is the story mainly about?

Text Structure

Let's **Think** About **Reading!**

- How is the story organized?
- Are there any patterns?

Visualize

Let's Think About Reading!

- What pictures do I see in my mind?

Program Authors

Peter Afflerbach

Camille Blachowicz

Candy Dawson Boyd

Elena Izquierdo

Connie Juel

Edward Kame'enui

Donald Leu

Jeanne R. Paratore

P. David Pearson

Sam Sebesta

Deborah Simmons

Alfred Tatum

Sharon Vaughn

Susan Watts Taffe

Karen Kring Wixson

 Glenview, Illinois • Boston, Massachusetts • Chandler, Arizona •
Upper Saddle River, New Jersey

We dedicate Reading Street to
Peter Jovanovich.

His wisdom, courage,
and passion for education
are an inspiration to us all.

About the Cover Artist
Daniel Moreton lives in New York City, where he uses his computer to create illustrations for books.
When he is not working, Daniel enjoys cooking, watching movies, and traveling. On a trip to Mexico,
Daniel was inspired by all of the bright colors around him. He likes to use those colors in his art.

ISBN-13: 978-0-328-39992-5
ISBN-10:   0-328-39992-2
2 3 4 5 6 7 8 9 10 V064 14 13 12 11 10
CC1

Dear Texas Reader,

How is your trip along *Scott Foresman Reading Street* so far? Have you enjoyed meeting all the characters?

As you go a little farther down *Reading Street*, you will meet more exciting characters, such as a pig in a wig, a blue ox, and a fox and a kit.

You will be reading articles and stories about tame animals and wild ones. And your reading will be getting better and better along the way!

Sincerely,
The Authors

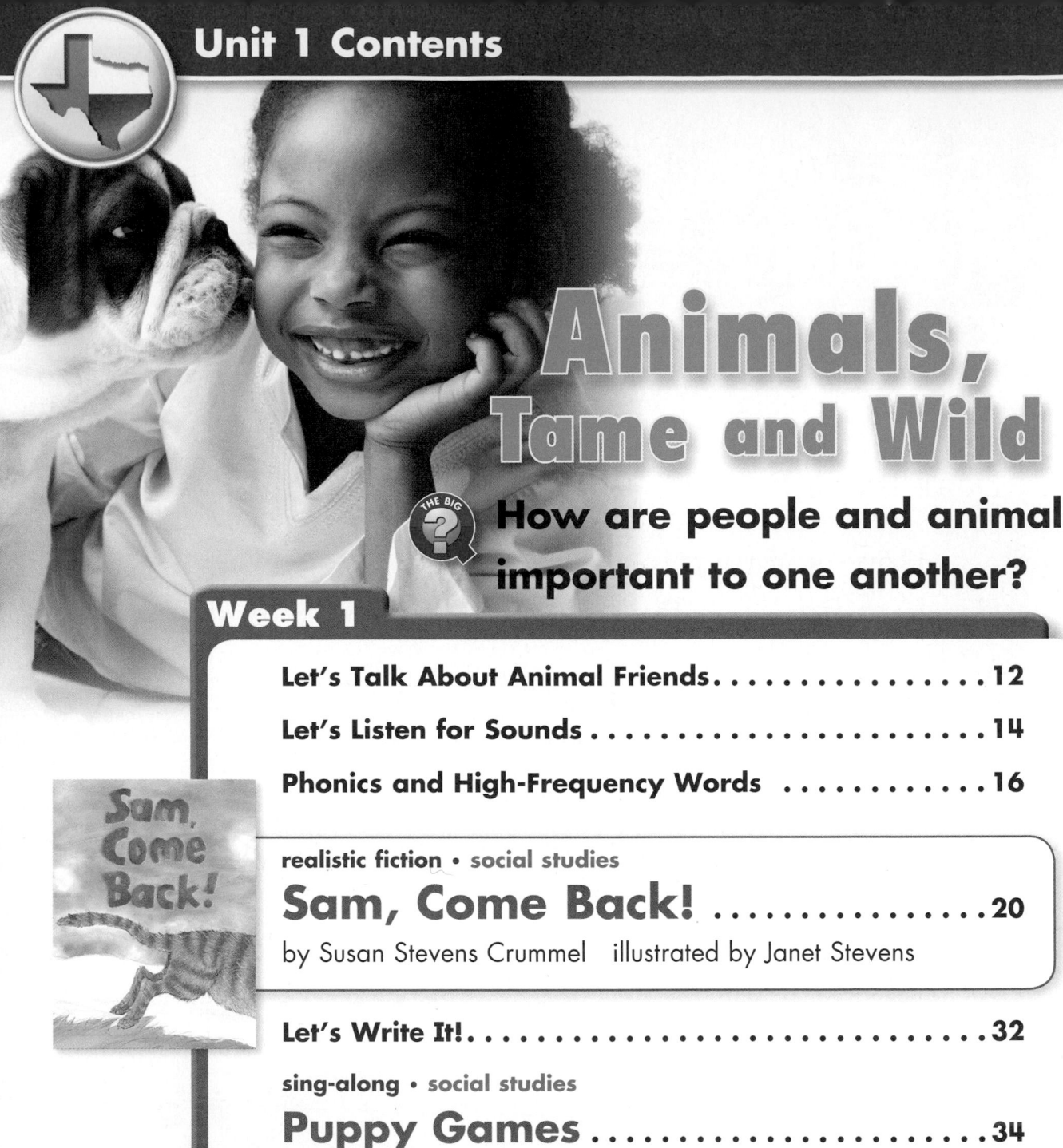

Animals, Tame and Wild

How are people and animals important to one another?

Week 2

Week 3

Unit 1 Contents

Week 6

Envision It! **A TEKS Comprehension Handbook**

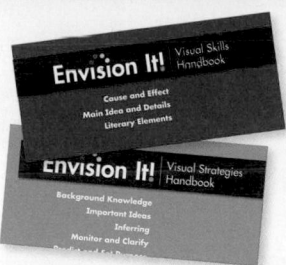

**Envision It! Visual Skills
Handbook EI•1–EI•6**

**Envision It! Visual Strategies
Handbook EI•7–EI•18**

Don Leu
The Internet Guy

Right before our eyes, the nature of reading and learning is changing. The Internet and other technologies create new opportunities, new solutions, and new literacies. New reading comprehension skills are required online. They are increasingly important to our students and our society.

Those of us on the Reading Street team are here to help you on this new, and very exciting, journey.

See It!

- **Big Question Video**

- **Concept Talk Video**

- **Envision It! Animations**

- **eReaders**

- **Interactive Sound-Spelling Cards**

Hear It!

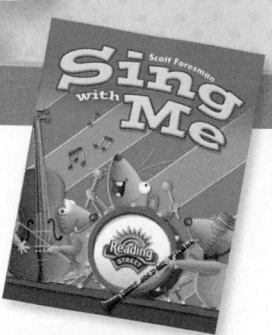

- **_Sing with Me_ Animations**

- **eSelections**

- **Grammar Jammer**

- **Vocabulary Activities**

Concept Talk Video

File   Edit   View   Favorites   Tools   Help

http://www.TexasReadingStreet.com

Do It!

- Journal Word Bank

- Story Sort

- Letter Tile Drag and Drop   o   s   c   m   s

- Online Assessment

- Vocabulary Activities

Animals, Tame and Wild

TEXAS
Reading Street Online
www.TexasReadingStreet.com
• Big Question Video
• eSelections
• Envision It! Animations
• Story Sort

THE BIG
?

How are people and animals important to one another?

TEKS

1.27.A.2 Ask relevant questions to clarify information. **1.28.A.2** Share ideas about the topic, speaking clearly at an appropriate pace, using the conventions of language. **Also 1.27.A.1, 1.28.A.1.**

Oral Vocabulary

Let's Talk About

Read Together

Animal Friends

- Share information about pets and other tame animals.

- Discuss the needs of pets.

READING STREET ONLINE
CONCEPT TALK VIDEO
www.TexasReadingStreet.com

13

TEKS

1.2.A.1 Orally generate a series of original rhyming words using a variety of phonograms. **1.2.D.1** Blend spoken phonemes to form one-syllable words, including consonant blends.

Phonemic Awareness

Let's Listen for

Sounds

- Find five things that contain the short *a* sound.

- Find five things that end with the sound /k/.

- Find something that rhymes with *luck*. Say each sound in the word.

- Find two things that rhyme with *pant*.

READING STREET ONLINE
SOUND-SPELLING CARDS
www.TexasReadingStreet.com

Read Together

COME IN

14

TEKS

1.3.A Decode words in context and in isolation by applying common letter-sound correspondences, including short *a*. **1.3.C.1.i** Use common syllabication patterns to decode words, including closed syllable (CVC). **Also 1.3.H.**

Envision It! | Sounds to Know

astronaut

short a

READING STREET ONLINE
SOUND-SPELLING CARDS
www.TexasReadingStreet.com

Phonics

Short *a: a*

Words I Can Blend

P	a	t
c	a	n
t	a	g
D	a	d
s	a	t

Sentences I Can Read

1. Pat can tag me.

2. Dad sat.

Words I Can Read

my

come

way

on

in

Sentences I Can Read

1. Sam can nap on my lap.

2. Dan can come in that way, Matt.

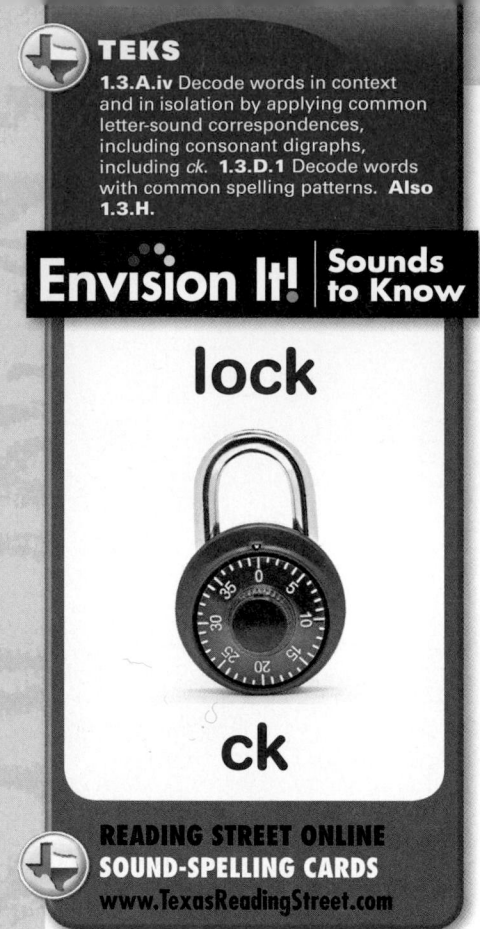

Envision It! | Sounds to Know

lock

ck

Phonics

Consonant Pattern *-ck*

Words I Can Blend

J a ck

b l a ck

s a ck

r a ck

b a ck

Sentences I Can Read

1. Hand Jack a black sack.

2. Can Dan nab that back rack?

I Can Read!

"I am Ann, an ant." Ann sat on a plant that my pal Jack Cat had.

Jack Cat ran in to pack for camp. "Can an ant come, Jack?" Can Jack Cat ask Dad?

Jack can ask Dad. "Pack Ann Ant! Ann Ant can camp!"

"Camp! Way to go, Jack!"

You've learned

- Short a: a
- Consonant Pattern -ck

High-Frequency Words

my   come   way   on   in

19

Sam, Come Back!

by Susan Stevens Crummel
illustrated by Janet Stevens

Realistic fiction tells about made-up events that could happen in real life. Next you will read about Sam and Jack, who are made-up characters.

Question of the Week

What do pets need?

21

Sam the cat is on my lap.

Sam ran. Sam, come back!

Sam ran that way.
Nab that cat!

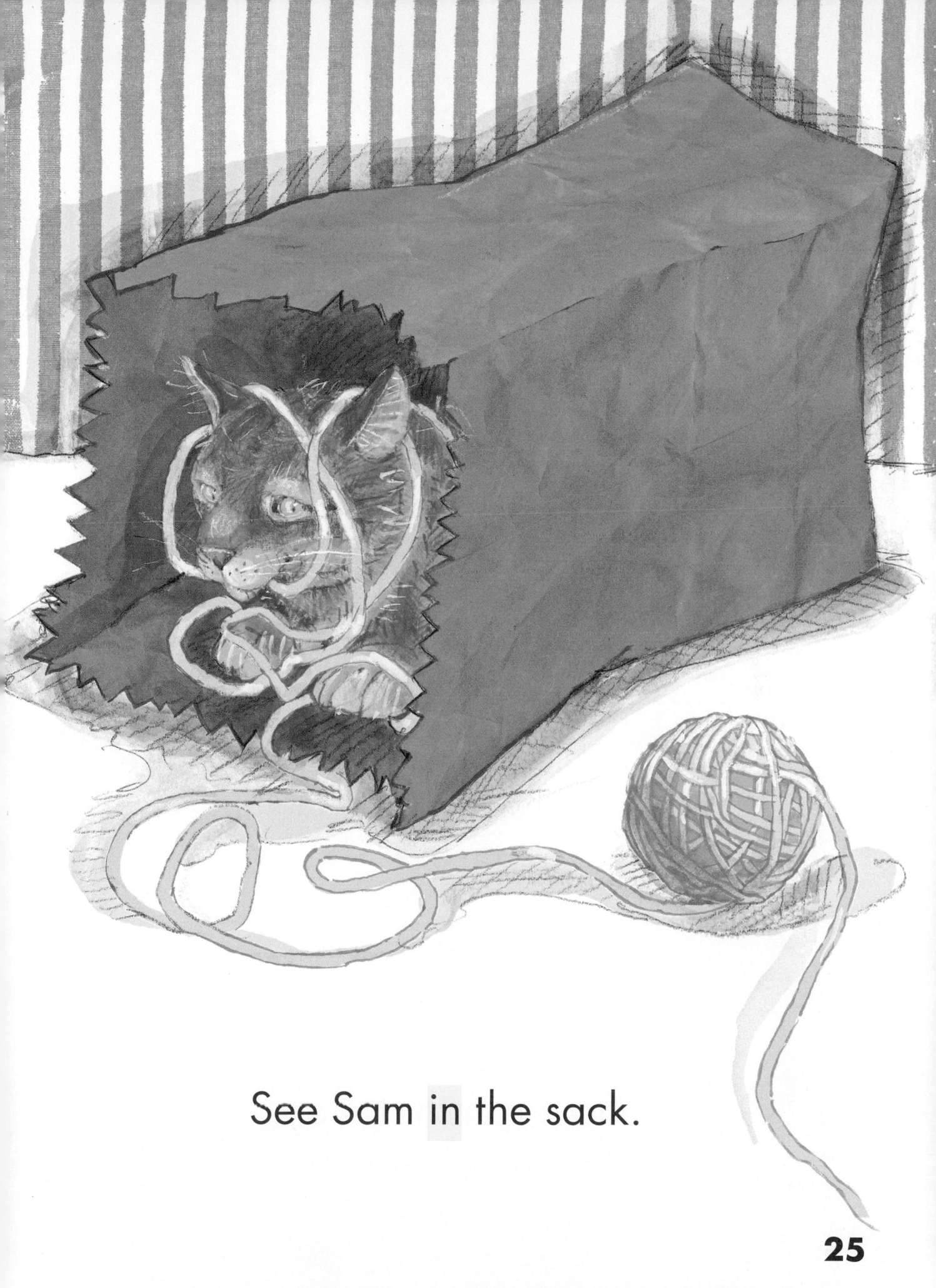

See Sam in the sack.

Sam ran that way.
Nab that cat!

See Sam in the pack.

Bad Sam! Sam, come back!

Jack, Jack! Sam is back.
Pat Sam on my lap.

TEKS
1.4.B.2 Seek clarification about stories and other texts. 1.9 Provide evidence from text to support understanding. 1.12.A.1 Read independently for a sustained period of time. Also 1.9.A.2, RC-1.F.1.

Envision It! Retell

Think Critically

Read Together

1. What part of the story do you think is funny? Why? **Text to Self**

2. Why do you think the author wrote this story? **Author's Purpose**

3. Where does Sam run? Why do you think he runs there?

   Character and Setting

4. Reread page 24. If you did not know what the word *nab* means, what could you do to figure it out?

   Monitor and Clarify

5. **Look Back and Write**
   Look back at page 25. Where does Sam run first? Write about it.

   TEST PRACTICE Extended Response

Susan Stevens Crummel

Susan Stevens Crummel loves all animals. Her cat, Tweeter, likes to sit in the chair by the computer.

Ms. Crummel wrote poems and songs when she was a child. She even wrote skits for her sister Janet to act out for friends.

Here are other books by Susan Stevens Crummel.

Use the Reading Log in the *Reader's and Writer's Notebook* to record your independent reading.

TEKS

1.18.A Write brief stories that include a beginning, middle, and end. **1.20.B** Speak in complete sentences with correct subject-verb agreement. **1.21.B** Recognize and use basic capitalization for the beginning of sentences. **Also 1.21.C.1, 1.21.C.4**

Let's Write It!

Key Features of a Story

- has characters and tells what they do

- is made of sentences

READING STREET ONLINE
GRAMMAR JAMMER
www.TexasReadingStreet.com

Narrative

Story

A **story** tells about characters. It tells what they do. The student model on the next page is an example of a story.

Writing Prompt Think about a pet you know. Write a story about the pet playing.

Writer's Checklist

Remember, you should . . .

☑ tell the kind of pet and what it does.

☑ show how you feel about the pet.

☑ begin each sentence with an uppercase, or capital, letter and end it with a period.

My Dog Rex

Rex has a toy duck.

He plays with it.

He puts it in his bed.

Rex is my best friend.

Sentences tell complete ideas. They begin with capital letters and end with periods.

Genre Story
The character is a dog named Rex.

Writing Trait Voice
The last sentence shows how the writer feels.

Conventions

● **Sentences**

Remember A **sentence** is a group of words that tells a complete idea. Say the sentence about the dog. **The dog is big.**

TEKS
1.8.A.1 Respond to rhythm in poetry.
1.8.A.2 Respond to rhyme in poetry.
1.8.A.4 Use rhythm in poetry.
1.8.A.5 Use rhyme in poetry.

Social Studies in Reading

Genre
Sing-Along

Read Together

- A sing-along is a song people sing together. Sometimes new words are sung to an old tune.

- A sing-along is a poem set to music. It has rhythm, or a regular pattern of beats.

- Some lines in a sing-along may repeat. Some words may rhyme.

- As you read "Puppy Games," think about what makes it a sing-along.

Sing to the tune of "Frère Jacques."

Puppy Games

by Linda Lott
illustrated by Maribel Suarez

Yap! Come play now!
Yap! Come play now!
Let's have fun.
Let's have fun.

34

I can tug on your socks.
I'll knock over your blocks.
Then I'll nap
In your lap.

Let's **Think** About...

What words in this sing-along rhyme? What is the sing-along's rhythm? Clap your hands to show it.
Sing-Along

Let's **Think** About...

Reading Across Texts How do the owners of Sam in *Sam, Come Back!* and the owner of the puppy in "Puppy Games" feel about their pets' actions?

Writing Across Texts Write sentences about what the puppy in the sing-along and Sam do. Use rhythm and rhyme.

TEKS

1.5.A.1 Read aloud grade-level appropriate text with fluency. **1.5.A.2** Read aloud grade-level appropriate text with comprehension. **1.6.D** Identify and sort words into conceptual categories. **1.27.A.1** Listen attentively to speakers. **1.27.A.2** Ask relevant questions to clarify information. ★ Understand and use words that name locations.

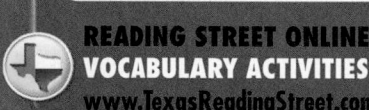

Let's Learn It!

Read Together

READING STREET ONLINE
VOCABULARY ACTIVITIES
www.TexasReadingStreet.com

Listening and Speaking

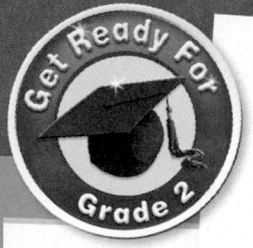

Get Ready For Grade 2

Ask a speaker questions if you don't understand something.

Ask Questions When someone is speaking, we listen carefully. If we do not understand something, we wait until the speaker is finished. Then we ask questions.

Practice It! Ask a partner to tell you about what pets need. Listen carefully. Ask questions to make sure you understand. Then tell your partner about what a pet needs. When your partner asks you questions, listen carefully to each one so that you know exactly what your partner is asking. Then answer the questions.

Vocabulary

Location words tell where things are.

a cat **over** a mat

a cat **under** a mat

Practice It! Read these words. Use each word to tell where something is.

on **up** **in** **out**

Fluency

Accuracy When you read, try to read with no mistakes.

Practice It!

1. Sam can come back.

2. Jack can snap the pack.

3. The black cat sat.

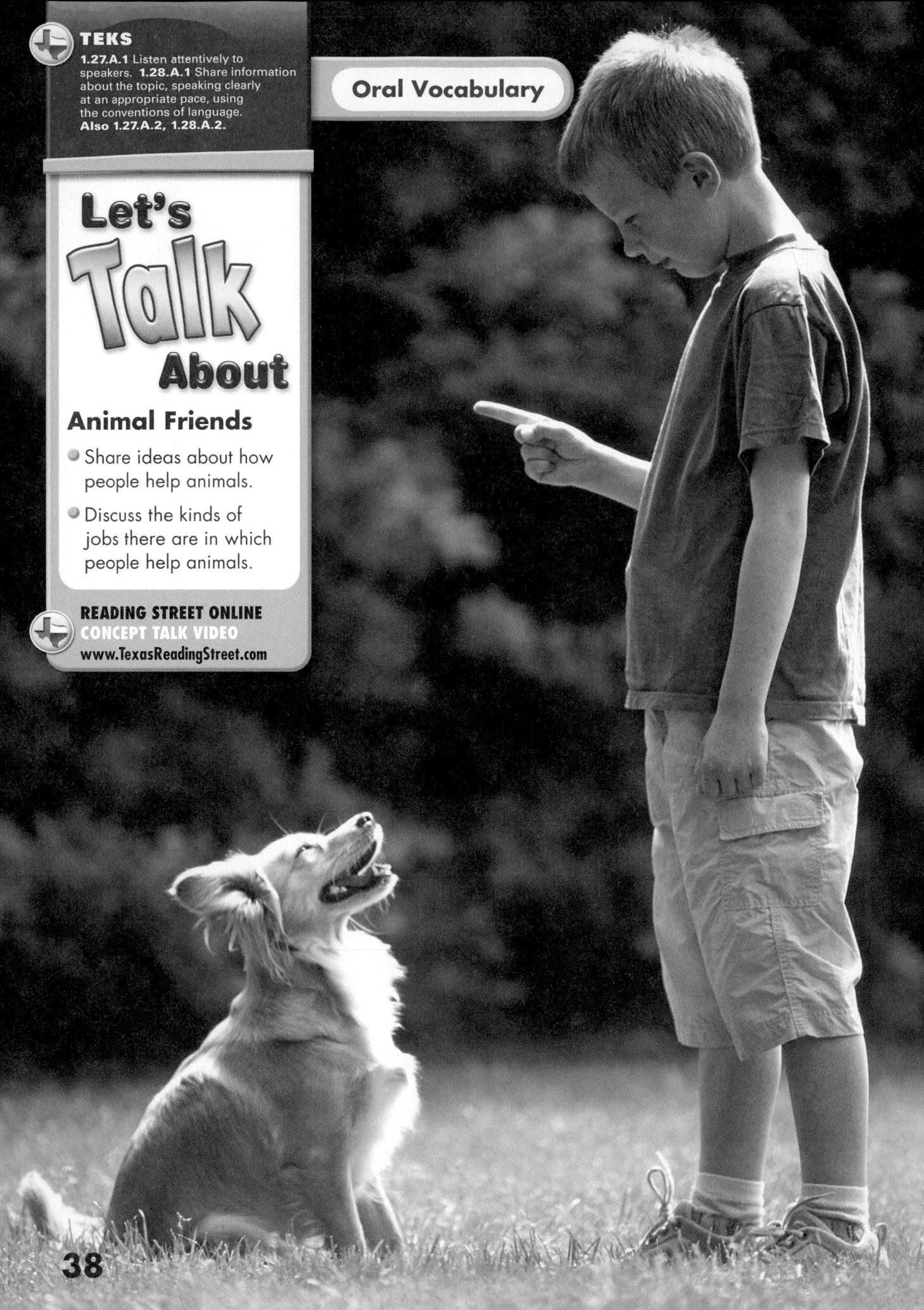

TEKS

1.27.A.1 Listen attentively to speakers. **1.28.A.1** Share information about the topic, speaking clearly at an appropriate pace, using the conventions of language. **Also 1.27.A.2, 1.28.A.2.**

Oral Vocabulary

Let's Talk About

Animal Friends

- Share ideas about how people help animals.

- Discuss the kinds of jobs there are in which people help animals.

READING STREET ONLINE
CONCEPT TALK VIDEO
www.TexasReadingStreet.com

TEKS
1.2.E.1 Isolate initial sounds in one-syllable spoken words. 1.2.F.1 Segment spoken one-syllable words of three to five phonemes into individual phonemes. Also 1.2.E.2, 1.2.E.3.

Phonemic Awareness

Let's Listen for

Sounds

Read Together

- Find five things that contain the short *i* sound in the middle of the word.

- Find something that has the short *i* sound at the beginning of the word. Say the word.

- Find four things that rhyme with *sick*. Say each word.

- Find something that rhymes with *six*. Say the sound at the end of that word.

- Find something that rhymes with *wish*. Say each sound in the word.

READING STREET ONLINE
SOUND-SPELLING CARDS
www.TexasReadingStreet.com

Ms. Ann

TEKS

1.3.A Decode words in context and in isolation by applying common letter-sound correspondences, including short *i*. 1.3.D.1 Decode words with common spelling patterns. **Also** 1.3.C.1.i and 1.3.H.

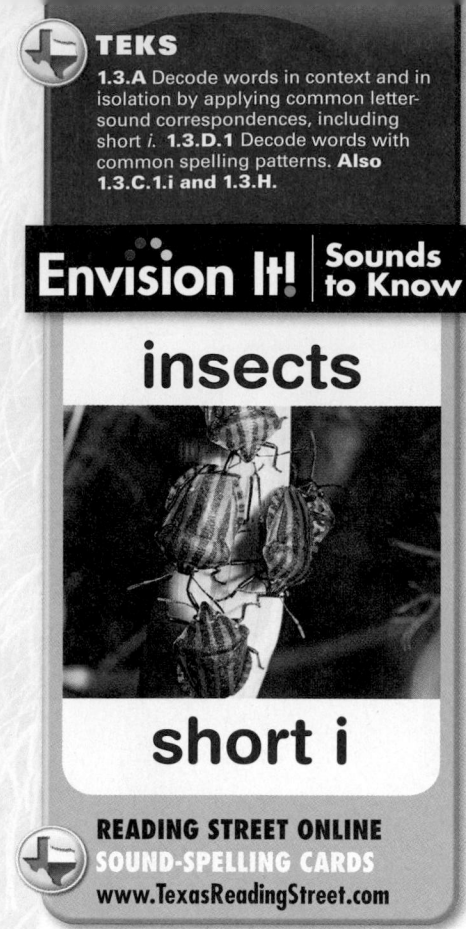

Envision It! | Sounds to Know

insects

short i

READING STREET ONLINE
SOUND-SPELLING CARDS
www.TexasReadingStreet.com

Phonics

Short *i*: *i*

Words I Can Blend

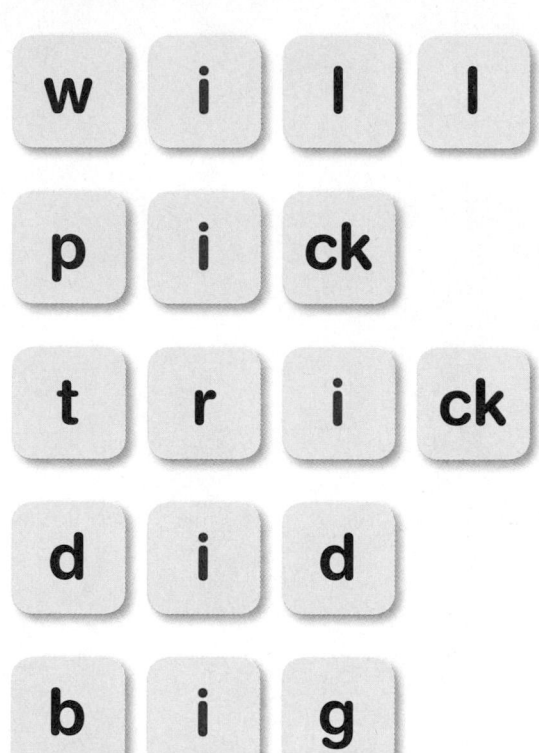

w i l l

p i ck

t r i ck

d i d

b i g

Sentences I Can Read

1. Dad will pick that trick.

2. Did that big bag sag?

Words I Can Read

she

take

what

up

Sentences I Can Read

1. She will take it back.

2. What did Bill pick up?

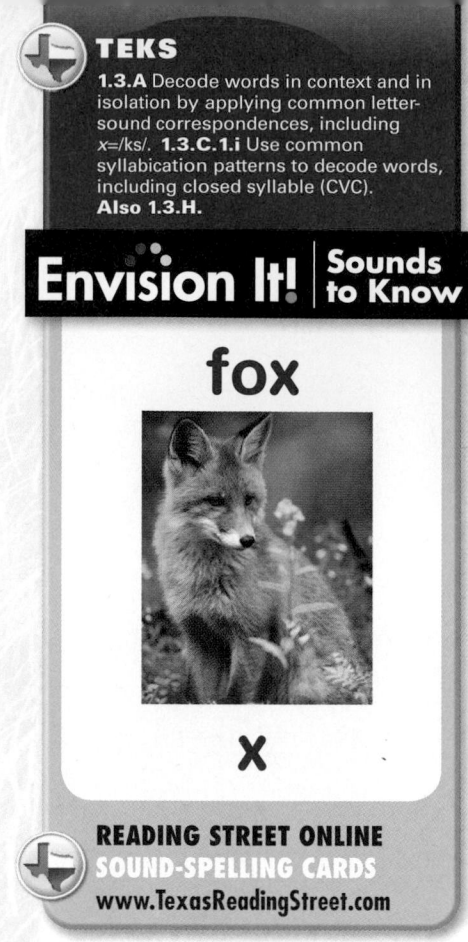

TEKS

1.3.A Decode words in context and in isolation by applying common letter-sound correspondences, including x=/ks/. **1.3.C.1.i** Use common syllabication patterns to decode words, including closed syllable (CVC). **Also 1.3.H.**

Envision It! | Sounds to Know

fox

x

READING STREET ONLINE
SOUND-SPELLING CARDS
www.TexasReadingStreet.com

Phonics

⟳ Consonant x/ks/

Words I Can Blend

M	a	x
f	i	x
s	a	x
m	i	x
s	i	x

Sentences I Can Read

1. Max will fix the sax.

2. Mix it at six.

I Can Read!

What can Nick fix? Quick, Nick! Fix the grill. Max can pick it up and take it with him.

Will Trix fix ham? She can fix it on the grill for Bill. It will fill him up.

Max will sit and sip milk. Milk will fill him up.

You've learned

- Short *i*: *i*
- Consonant *x*/ks/

High-Frequency Words
she   take   what   up

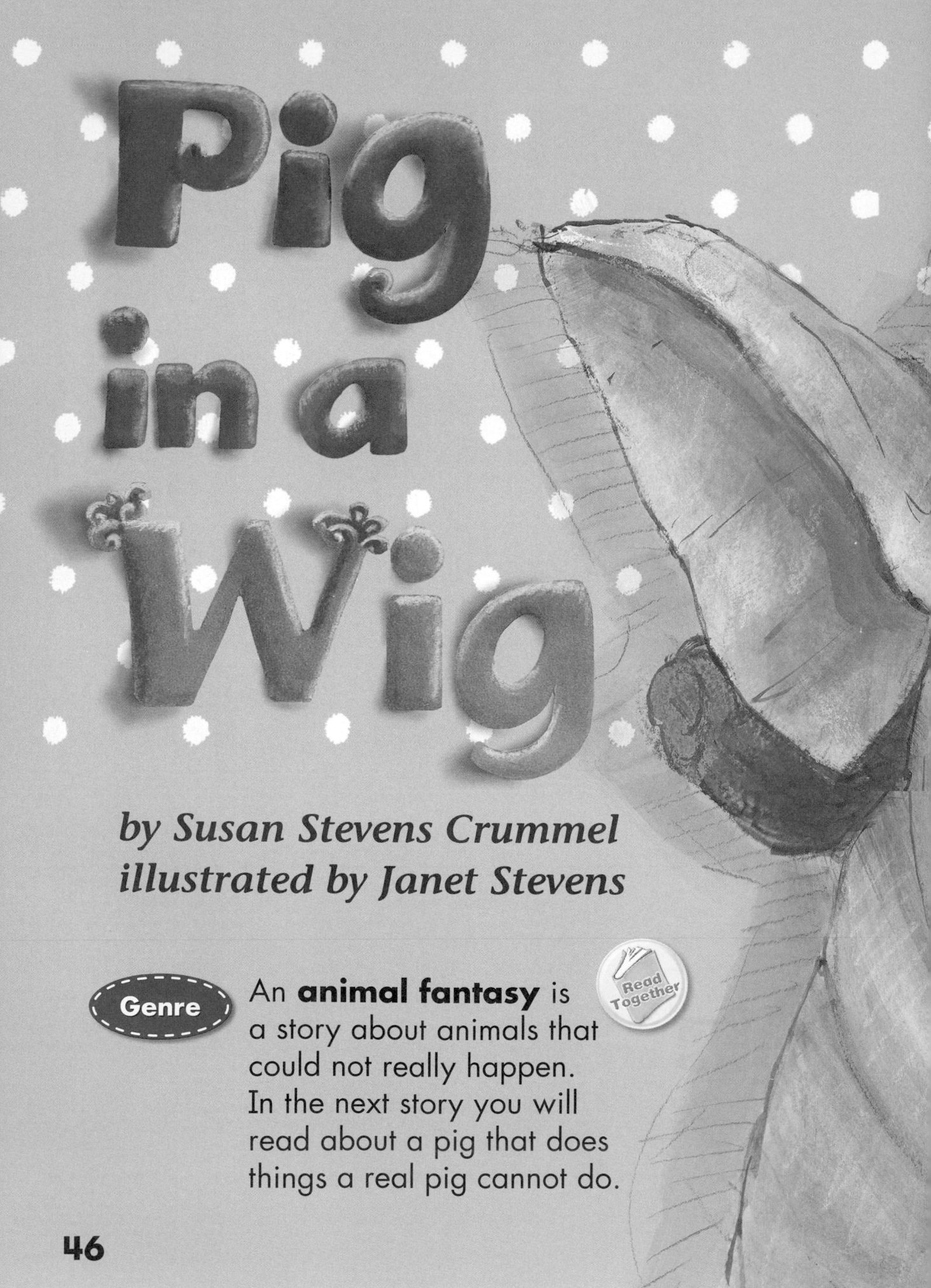

Pig in a Wig

by Susan Stevens Crummel
illustrated by Janet Stevens

Genre An **animal fantasy** is a story about animals that could not really happen. In the next story you will read about a pig that does things a real pig cannot do.

Read Together

46

Question of the Week

Who helps animals?

Pig in a wig is big, you see.

Tick, tick, tick.
It is three.

Pig can mix.
Mix it up.

Pig can dip.
Dip it up.

Pig can lick.
Lick it up.

It is six. Tick, tick, tick.
Pig is sad. She is sick.

Fix that pig.
Take a sip.

Fix that pig.
Quick, quick, quick!

Max, Max! Take the sax!
Play it, Max, and play it, Pam!

Pig in a wig did a jig.
What a ham!

TEKS
1.9 Provide evidence from text to support understanding. **1.12.A.1** Read independently for a sustained period of time. **Also 1.9.A.2, RC-1.E.1, RC-1.F.3.**

Envision It! Retell

Think Critically

1. How is Pig like Sam in *Sam, Come Back!*? Text to Text

2. How does the author make Pig seem silly? Think Like an Author

3. What problem does Pig have? How does Pig solve the problem? Plot

4. Tell about the important events in the story. Summarize

5. Look Back and Write Look back at page 57. How does Pig feel? Write about it. Use evidence from the story.

TEST PRACTICE Extended Response

Janet Stevens

Janet Stevens always wanted to draw pictures. She enjoys drawing pictures for children's books.

Ms. Stevens practices drawing all the time. "Practice helps a lot in whatever you try to do," she says. She likes to draw pigs, cats, and bears.

Here are other books illustrated by Janet Stevens.

To Market, To Market
Anne Miranda
ILLUSTRATED BY Janet Stevens

EPOSSUMONDAS
WRITTEN BY Coleen Salley
ILLUSTRATED BY Janet Stevens

Reading Log

Use the Reading Log in the *Reader's and Writer's Notebook* to record your independent reading.

TEKS

1.18.A Write brief stories that include a beginning, middle, and end. **1.21.B.i** Recognize and use basic capitalization for the beginning of sentences. **1.21.C.4** Use punctuation marks at the end of declarative sentences. **Also 1.21.C.1**

Let's Write It!

Key Features of a Fantasy Story

- characters and events are made up

- characters do things that real people and animals cannot do

 READING STREET ONLINE
GRAMMAR JAMMER
www.TexasReadingStreet.com

Narrative

Fantasy Story

A **fantasy story** has events that cannot really happen. The student model on the next page is an example of a fantasy story.

Writing Prompt Write a fantasy story about a person who helps an animal. Draw a picture for your story.

Writer's Checklist

Remember, you should . . .

☑ use your imagination to write and draw a picture.

☑ begin each sentence with a capital letter and end it with a period.

☑ make sure each sentence has a subject.

The Pet Cow

Bob has a pet cow.

Cow likes to cook.

It makes a big mess.

Bob gives Cow a bath.

Each sentence has a **subject.**

Writing Trait Conventions Sentences begin with capital letters and end with periods.

Genre Fantasy Story A real cow cannot cook.

Conventions

● **Subjects of Sentences**

Remember A sentence has a **subject,** or naming part.

The pig did a jig.

61

TEKS

1.8.A.1 Respond to rhythm in poetry.
1.8.A.2 Respond to rhyme in poetry.
1.8.A.4 Use rhythm in poetry.
1.8.A.5 Use rhyme in poetry.

Social Studies in Reading

Genre
Sing-Along

Read Together

- A song people sing together is sometimes called a sing-along. New words may be sung to a well-known tune.

- A sing-along is a poem set to music. It has clear rhythm, and some of the words may rhyme.

- Kids might sing a sing-along during a long car ride with their families or at summer camp with other kids.

- Read "We Are Vets." As you read, look for elements that make it a sing-along.

We Are Vets

by Linda Lott
illustrated by Lindsey Gardiner

Sing to the tune of "Three Blind Mice."

We are vets.

We are vets.

We help pets.

We help pets.

If you have a dog who
    is feeling sick,

Bring him to me, and I'll
    fix him quick.

His tail will wag, and
    he'll chase a stick.

He'll feel fine. He'll feel fine.

Let's **Think** About...

Which words rhyme in this sing-along? What is its rhythm?
Sing-Along

Let's **Think** About...

Reading Across Texts The pig in *Pig in a Wig* and the dog in "We Are Vets" both feel sick. Who helps them get better? How?

Writing Across Texts Write a poem about what the two animals do after they get better. Use rhythm and rhyme in your poem.

TEKS

1.5.A.1 Read aloud grade-level appropriate text with fluency. **1.5.A.2** Read aloud grade-level appropriate text with comprehension. **1.6.E.1** Alphabetize a series of words to the first letter. **1.28.A.2** Share ideas about the topic, speaking clearly at an appropriate pace, using the conventions of language. **1.29.A.1** Follow agreed-upon rules for discussion, including listening to others. **Also 1.29.A.2.**

Let's Learn It!

Read Together

READING STREET ONLINE VOCABULARY ACTIVITIES
www.TexasReadingStreet.com

Get Ready For Grade 2

Listen carefully when others are speaking.

Listening and Speaking

Share Information and Ideas When we tell others our ideas, we speak clearly so that they understand us. When others tell us their ideas, we listen so that we understand them.

Practice It! When asked, tell others how you care for an animal. Then let them tell you how they care for an animal. Follow the rules. Listen carefully. Take notes to help you understand.

Vocabulary

These words are in **alphabetical order.** Look at the first letter in each word. Think about the alphabet.

ant

bat

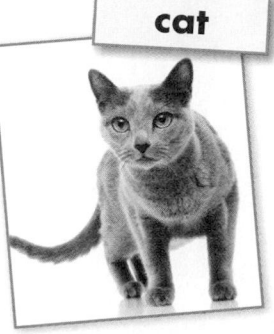

cat

Practice It! Read these words. Write them in alphabetical order.

big   **dip**   **am**   **can**

Fluency

Accuracy When you read, try to read with no mistakes.

Practice It!

1. Max can mix it.

2. The black cat licks Bill.

3. She will take the sack.

TEKS

1.27.A.1 Listen attentively to speakers. **1.28.A.1** Share information about the topic, speaking clearly at an appropriate pace, using the conventions of language. **Also 1.27.A.2, 1.28.A.2.**

Oral Vocabulary

Let's Talk About

Read Together

Animal Friends

- Contribute to a discussion about the kinds of animals that help people.

- Share information about how animals help people.

READING STREET ONLINE CONCEPT TALK VIDEO www.TexasReadingStreet.com

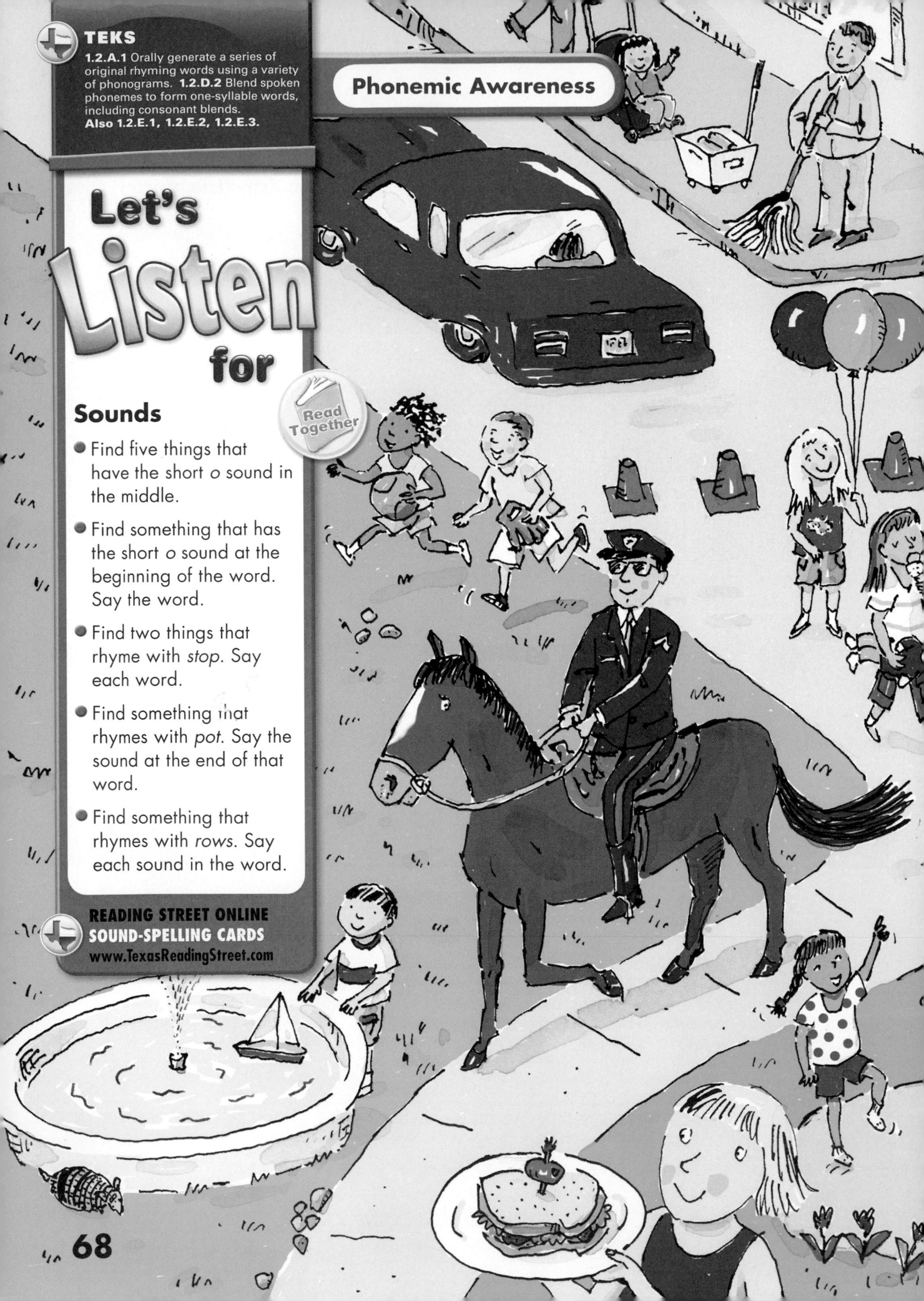

TEKS

1.2.A.1 Orally generate a series of original rhyming words using a variety of phonograms. **1.2.D.2** Blend spoken phonemes to form one-syllable words, including consonant blends. **Also 1.2.E.1, 1.2.E.2, 1.2.E.3.**

Phonemic Awareness

Let's Listen for

Sounds

Read Together

- Find five things that have the short *o* sound in the middle.

- Find something that has the short *o* sound at the beginning of the word. Say the word.

- Find two things that rhyme with *stop*. Say each word.

- Find something that rhymes with *pot*. Say the sound at the end of that word.

- Find something that rhymes with *rows*. Say each sound in the word.

**READING STREET ONLINE
SOUND-SPELLING CARDS
www.TexasReadingStreet.com**

$10.00
$5.00

Bakery

69

TEKS

1.3.A Decode words in context and in isolation by applying common letter-sound correspondences, including single letter short o. **1.3.C.1.i** Use common syllabication patterns to decode words, including closed syllable (CVC). **Also 1.3.H.**

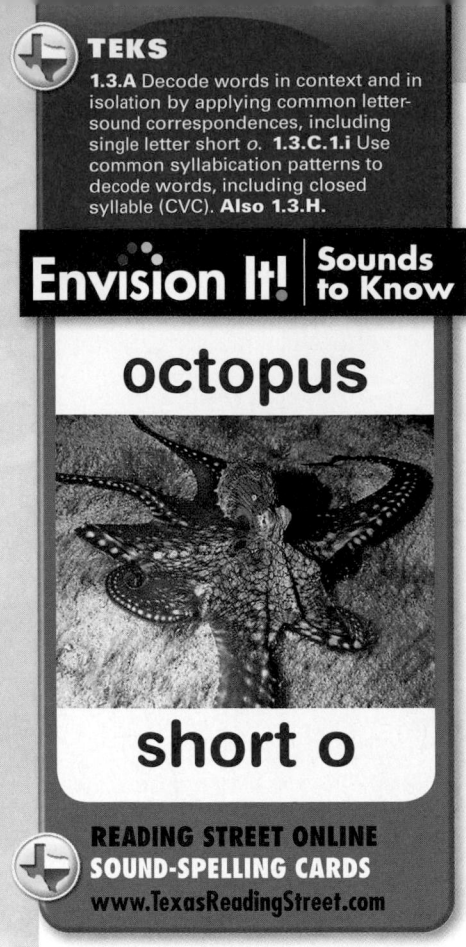

Envision It! | **Sounds to Know**

octopus

short o

READING STREET ONLINE SOUND-SPELLING CARDS
www.TexasReadingStreet.com

Phonics

Short o: o

Words I Can Blend

| s | o | ck |

| o | n |

| D | o | t |

| l | o | ck |

| b | o | x |

Sentences I Can Read

1. Jan can fit that sock on Dot.

2. Lock that big box.

Words I Can Read

blue

help

little

from

use

get

Sentences I Can Read

1. Help him fix the little blue clock.

2. Get the mop from Jon and use it.

TEKS
1.3.A Decode words in context and in isolation by applying common letter-sound correspondences, including single letter s=/z/. **1.3.E.1** Read base words with inflectional endings. Also **1.3.H.**

dogs

plural -s

cars

s

READING STREET ONLINE
SOUND-SPELLING CARDS
www.TexasReadingStreet.com

Phonics

Plural -s, Consonant s/z/

Words I Can Blend

Sentences I Can Read

1. Mom will grab sticks and rocks.

2. Kids can drop socks in bags.

Tom is on my block. His job is to help little kids get help from big kids. Lots of kids can use help.

Kip can spot his blue block drop in Fox Pond. Rob and Tom got it.

Wags can drag socks in the sand. Rob and Tom will stop that. Rob and Tom did big jobs.

You've learned

- Short o: o
- Plural -s, Consonant s/z/

High-Frequency Words
blue   help   little
    from   use   get

The Big Blue Ox

by Susan Stevens Crummel

illustrated by Janet Stevens

Genre

Read Together

An **animal fantasy** is a make-believe story with animals that act like people. Next you will read about an ox that acts like a person. What do you want to find out? Set a purpose for reading.

Question of the Week

How do animals help people?

Mom and Pop have a big blue ox.

Ox can help. He is big.
He can pick, and he can dig.

Pigs in wigs sit in mud.
Ox can help a little!

Get the mop from Mom and Pop.
Mop the pigs. Fix the wigs.

Off to town go Mom and Pop.
Ox can help! Hop on top.

Get the cans. Pack the sack.
Ox can help! Take it back.

Ox can help! Use big pans.
He is hot. Use big fans!

Mom and Pop nap on Ox.
Ox is a big, big help.

TEKS
1.9 Provide evidence from text to support understanding. **1.12.A.1** Read independently for a sustained period of time. **1.19.C.1** Write brief comments on literary texts. **Also 1.9.A.2, RC-1.D.2, RC-1.E.1, RC-1.F.1, RC-1.F.4.**

Envision It! Retell

READING STREET ONLINE STORY SORT
www.TexasReadingStreet.com

Think Critically

1. Ox is a helpful friend. How do you help your friends and family? Text to Self

2. Why do you think the author decided Ox would be big? Author's Purpose

3. Who are the characters in this story? Where does this story take place?

   Character and Setting

4. What pictures did you see in your mind of Ox helping?

   Visualize

5. **Look Back and Write** Look back at pages 79–82. Write some things Ox can do to help. Be sure to use evidence from the story.

    TEST PRACTICE Extended Response

Susan Stevens Crummel and Janet Stevens

Susan Stevens Crummel and Janet Stevens are sisters! They have fun working together. Ms. Crummel writes down ideas and turns them into a story. She sends the story to her sister Janet, who draws pictures to fit the story.

Here are other books written and illustrated by Susan Stevens Crummel and Janet Stevens.

COOK-A-DOODLE-DOO!
Janet Stevens and Susan Stevens Crummel

JANET STEVENS AND SUSAN STEVENS CRUMMEL
And the DISH Ran Away with the SPOON
ILLUSTRATED BY Janet Stevens

Reading Log Use the Reading Log in the *Reader's and Writer's Notebook* to record your independent reading.

85

TEKS
1.18.B.1 Write short poems that convey sensory details. **1.20.B.1** Speak in complete sentences with correct subject-verb agreement.

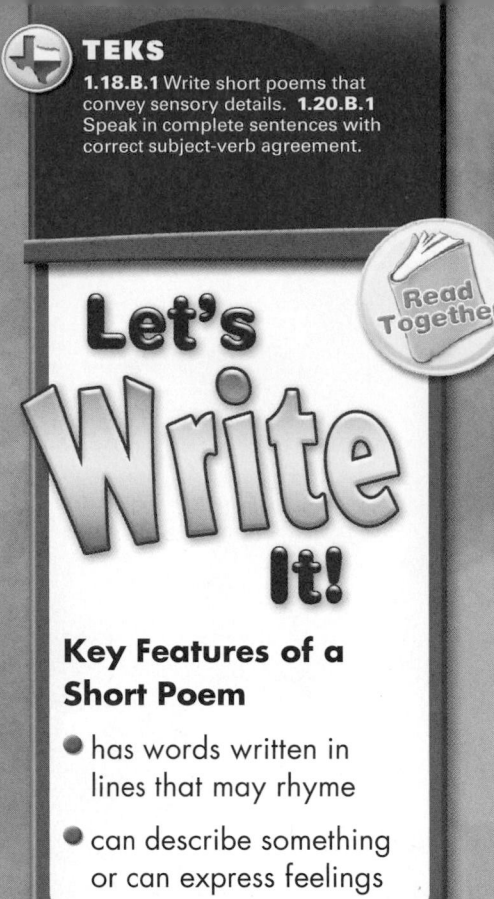

Let's Write It!

Read Together

Key Features of a Short Poem

- has words written in lines that may rhyme
- can describe something or can express feelings

**READING STREET ONLINE
GRAMMAR JAMMER**
www.TexasReadingStreet.com

Descriptive

Short Poem

A **short poem** has words written in lines. In many poems, the lines rhyme. The student model on the next page shows two examples of short poems.

Writing Prompt Think about a kind of animal you know. Write a two-line poem about that animal.

Writer's Checklist

Remember, you should . . .

☑ write a poem two lines long about a kind of animal.

☑ make the lines rhyme if you wish. Say the sentences.

☑ make sure each sentence you say has a predicate.

A Fast Cat

Can a cat run up a hill?

Yes, yes, a fast cat will.

A Hen

A hen ran up to the men.

A man fed corn to the hen.

**Writing Trait
Sentences**
A sentence tells
a complete idea.

The **predicate**
of the sentence
tells what
someone does.

**Genre
Short Poem**
Read a **poem**
aloud. In the
sentences, words
that rhyme
sound alike.

Conventions

- ## Predicates of Sentences

Remember A sentence has a
predicate, a telling part. It tells what a
person or thing does. Say the sentences.

Ox **helps Mom and Pop.** He **sits.**

87

TEKS

1.16 Use comprehension skills to analyze how words, images, graphics, and sounds work together in various forms to impact meaning.

Social Studies in Reading

Genre
Photo Essay

Read Together

- A photo essay is made up of photographs and words about one topic. The photographs help readers understand the words.

- Photographs can help readers connect with real people, places, and events.

- The photographs in a photo essay are usually displayed on the pages in a creative way.

- As you read "They Can Help," think about what makes it a photo essay.

They Can Help

by Pat Waris

We can use help.
Can we get help?

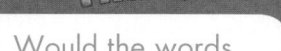
Let's **Think** About...

Would the words on these pages make sense without the photographs? Why or why not?
Photo Essay

The big dog can help.

The little dog can help.

Let's **Think** About...

How do these photographs show what the words are telling?
Photo Essay

Let's **Think** About...

Retell the order of events in the text using the words.
Photo Essay

The big dog can help.

The little dog can help.

In what ways do they help?

Let's Think About...

How do these photographs answer the question on the page? **Photo Essay**

Let's Think About...

Reading Across Texts How are Ox in *The Big Blue Ox* and the animals in "They Can Help" different? How are the ways they help people different?

Writing Across Texts Draw pictures of Ox helping and an animal in the photo essay helping. Write sentences that tell what they are doing.

TEKS

1.5.A.1 Read aloud grade-level appropriate text with fluency. **1.5.A.2** Read aloud grade-level appropriate text with comprehension. **1.6.D** Identify and sort words into conceptual categories. **1.28.A.1** Share information about the topic, speaking clearly at an appropriate pace, using the conventions of language.
★ Identify and use common words that are similar (synonyms) in meaning.

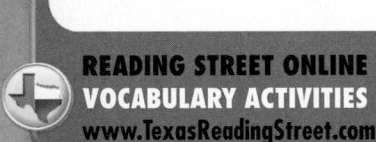

Let's **Learn** It!

Read Together

READING STREET ONLINE
VOCABULARY ACTIVITIES
www.TexasReadingStreet.com

Micah, this is Sara. Sara is in my class. She likes to play soccer just like you!

Get Ready For Grade 2

Speak clearly when introducing people.

Listening and Speaking

Give Introductions When we introduce someone to someone else, we say both of their names. We tell something about the two people. We make sure to speak clearly.

Practice It! Practice introducing friends. Say both of their names clearly. Remember something you know about your friends and tell it to them.

Vocabulary

A **synonym** is a word that means the same or almost the same thing as another word.

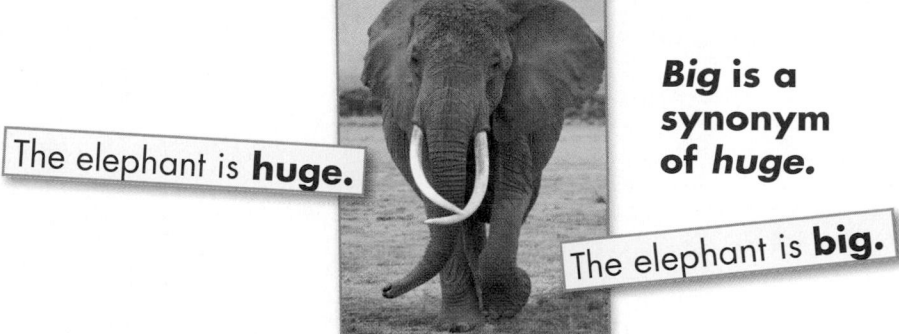

The elephant is **huge.**

Big is a synonym of *huge.*

The elephant is **big.**

Practice It! Read these words. Write the words that are synonyms next to each other.

small   **quick**   **fast**   **little**

Fluency

Rate When you read, try to read the sentences as if you are talking. Think about what the sentences mean.

Practice It!

1. Tom can get the hats from Mom.

2. Use a box to pack the blue hats.

3. Pop can help get a box of wigs.

TEKS

1.27.A.1 Listen attentively to speakers. **1.28.A.1** Share information about the topic, speaking clearly at an appropriate pace, using the conventions of language.
Also 1.27.A.2, 1.28.A.2.

Let's Talk About

Wild Animals

- Share information about wild animals.

- Discuss how wild animals take care of their babies.

READING STREET ONLINE
CONCEPT TALK VIDEO
www.TexasReadingStreet.com

95

TEKS
1.2.D.1 Blend spoken phonemes to form one-syllable words. **1.2.D.2** Blend spoken phonemes to form two-syllable words. **1.2.F.1** Segment spoken one-syllable words of three to five phonemes into individual phonemes.

Let's Listen for

Sounds

Read Together

- Find five people who are doing something. Tell what they are doing.

- Find two actions that rhyme with *ends*. Say the sounds in each word.

- Find two actions that rhyme with *pumping*. Say the sounds in each word.

READING STREET ONLINE
SOUND-SPELLING CARDS
www.TexasReadingStreet.com

Envision It! | Sounds to Know

pulls

ending -s

READING STREET ONLINE
SOUND-SPELLING CARDS
www.TexasReadingStreet.com

Phonics

Inflected Ending -s

Words I Can Blend

s i t s

a d d s

t a g s

g r i n s

c l a p s

Sentences I Can Read

1. Lin sits and adds as Pat tags Jill.

2. Kim grins and claps.

Words I Can Read

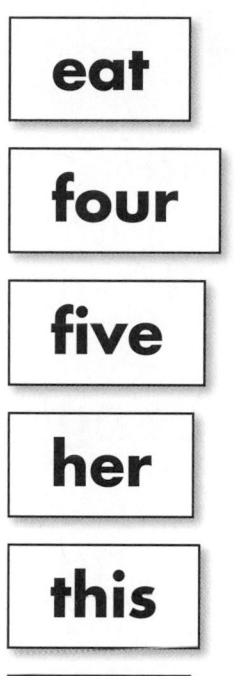

eat

four

five

her

this

too

Sentences I Can Read

1. Four kids eat yams, and Jan snacks on five ham bits too.

2. This is a big hat that fits her.

Envision It! | Sounds to Know

drinking

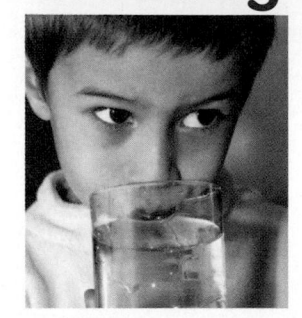

ending -ing

Phonics

Inflected Ending *-ing*

Words I Can Blend

p a ck i ng

c a m p i ng

m i s s i ng

h a n d i ng

s p i l l i ng

Sentences I Can Read

1. Mack is packing for his camping trip and missing Mom.

2. Will is handing his glass to Sam and spilling his milk.

I Can Read!

Fran has a list. Fran fills it with five jobs. Fran has to eat. Doll has to eat too. That is two jobs.

Fran sits and adds. That is three jobs.

Fran is filling her pack. That is four jobs.

Fran naps. This is her last job. Fran is passing the list to Jan.

You've learned

- Inflected Ending -s
- Inflected Ending -ing

High-Frequency Words

eat	four	five
her	this	too

A Fox and a Kit

by Leya Roberts

illustrated by Charles Santore

RED FOX

Genre **Literary nonfiction** tells facts about the real world. It is sometimes told like a story. You will read about a fox and her kit at the zoo.

How do wild animals take care of their babies?

It is four.

This fox naps on the rocks.

Her kit naps on the rocks too.

The kit sits up.
His mom sits up.

It is five.
This man is fixing dinner.
The kit and his mom will eat.

The kit is licking his lips.
His mom is licking her lips.

The kit is playing.
His mom is playing.
The kit nips and tags his mom.

The kit is on the rocks.
His mom will get him.
She picks him up and takes him back.

The kit spots his mom.
His mom spots him.

We like to watch this kit and
his mom!
We can watch lots of animals.

TEKS

1.10 Provide evidence from text to support understanding. **1.12.A.1** Read independently for a sustained period of time. **Also RC-1.D.2, RC-1.E.1, RC-1.F.3, RC-1.F.4.**

Envision It! | Retell

Think Critically

1. *A Fox and a Kit* is about a mother fox and her kit. Tell about how another animal mother takes care of her baby. Text to World

2. What does the author want you to learn by reading this selection? Author's Purpose

3. What is the selection mostly about? Main Idea and Details

4. What did you learn about foxes by reading this selection? Important Ideas

5. **Look Back and Write** Look back at page 109. Write about how the fox takes care of her kit. Use evidence from the selection.

 TEST PRACTICE Extended Response

Charles Santore

Charles Santore went to a zoo to learn about foxes. Mr. Santore also put pictures of foxes all around his studio to help him paint the pictures he needed for this story. Animals are a big part of his work.

Here are other books illustrated by Charles Santore.

Use the Reading Log in the *Reader's and Writer's Notebook* to record your independent reading.

113

TEKS

1.18.A.1 Write brief stories that include a beginning, middle, and end. **1.21.C.1** Recognize punctuation marks at the end of declarative sentences. **1.21.C.4** Use punctuation marks at the end of declarative sentences.

Let's Write It!

Read Together

Key Features of a Personal Narrative

- tells a story about a real event in the author's life
- tells how the author feels about it

READING STREET ONLINE
GRAMMAR JAMMER
www.TexasReadingStreet.com

Narrative

Personal Narrative

A **personal narrative** tells of an event in the author's life. The student model on the next page is an example of a personal narrative.

Writing Prompt Think about a time you watched some animals. Write a narrative about it.

Writer's Checklist

Remember, you should . . .

☑ write about a time when you saw an animal or animals.

☑ use words that tell how you felt about what happened.

☑ write sentences that tell about the event from the beginning to the end.

The Ducks

Once I saw two ducks.

They swam in the pond.

They ate plants.

I wanted to swim!

I like to see ducks.

Writing Trait Voice
Your writing tells how you feel. This writer shows feelings.

Genre
This **personal narrative** tells about an event that happened in the writer's own life.

A **declarative sentence** begins with a capital letter and ends with a period.

Conventions

- **Declarative Sentences**

- **Remember** A **declarative sentence** is a telling sentence. It begins with a capital letter and ends with a period.

115

TEKS

1.7.A.2 Connect the meaning of a well-known fable to personal experiences.

Science in Reading

Genre
Fable

Read Together

- A fable is a short story that teaches a lesson, or moral.

- The characters in a fable are often animals that speak and act like people.

- The author wants readers to connect a fable's moral to their personal experiences.

- Read "The Fox and the Grapes." Look for elements that make this story a fable.

The Fox and the Grapes

adapted from Aesop

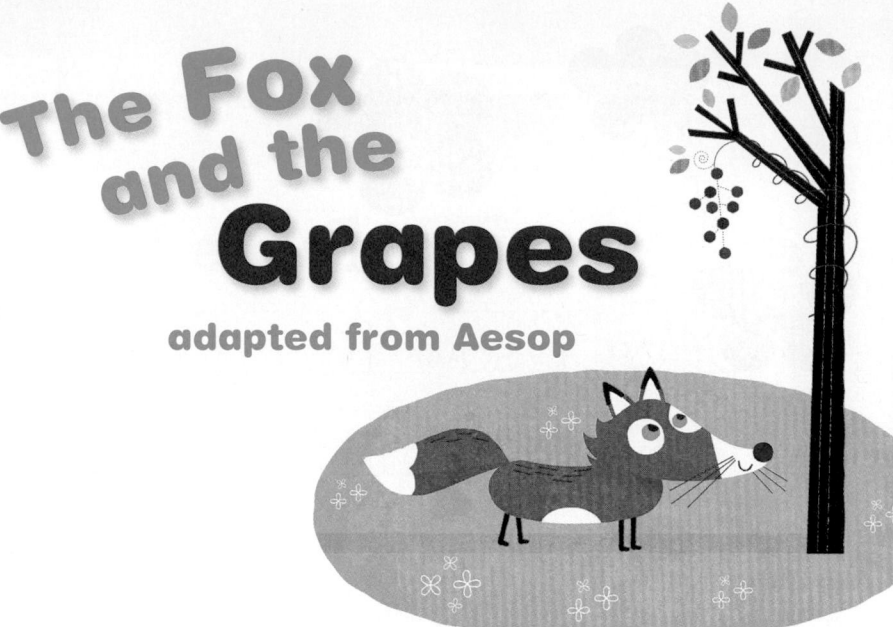

One day, a fox wanted grapes.

But he could not reach them.

The fox tried again and again.

At last, the fox gave up.

"I did not want those sour grapes anyway," he said.

Moral: It is easy to dislike what you cannot get.

Let's **Think** About...

How do you know this story is a fable? **Fable**

Let's **Think** About...

What does the moral of the fable mean? How can you connect the meaning to things that have happened to you? **Fable**

Let's **Think** About...

Reading Across Texts How are the foxes in *A Fox and a Kit* and "The Fox and the Grapes" alike? How are they different?

Writing Across Texts Imagine the foxes in *A Fox and a Kit* could talk to the fox in "The Fox and the Grapes." Write what they would say to him. Write what he would say to them.

TEKS

1.5.A.1 Read aloud grade-level appropriate text with fluency. **1.5.A.2** Read aloud grade-level appropriate text with comprehension. **1.6.E.2** Alphabetize a series of words to the second letter. **1.29.A.1** Follow agreed-upon rules for discussion, including listening to others. **1.29.A.3** Follow agreed-upon rules for discussion, including making appropriate contributions. **Also 1.20.B.1, 1.27.A.1, 1.27.A.2.**

READING STREET ONLINE
VOCABULARY ACTIVITIES
www.TexasReadingStreet.com

Listening and Speaking

Stay on topic when you speak.

Share Information and Ideas When we share ideas with others, we speak clearly. We listen carefully to other ideas. We ask questions if we need more information.

Practice It! Discuss your favorite animal. Speak clearly in sentences. Stay on topic during the discussion. Listen carefully, take notes, and ask questions if you do not understand something.

118

Vocabulary

When we put words in **alphabetical order,** we look at the first letter in each word. Then we think about the alphabet and remember which letter comes first. If two words start with the same letter, we look at the second letter.

Practice It! Read these words. Write them in alphabetical order.

dog   sit   tan   step

Fluency

Rate When you read, try to read the sentences as if you were talking. Don't read too quickly or too slowly.

Practice It!

1. Tim can help by packing this bag.

2. The cat eats and naps.

3. The fox naps too.

TEKS

1.27.A.2 Ask relevant questions to clarify information. **1.28.A.2** Share ideas about the topic, speaking clearly at an appropriate pace, using the conventions of language. **Also 1.27.A.1, 1.28.A.1.**

Let's Talk About

Read Together

Wild Animals

- Take part in a discussion about wild animals that live in our neighborhood.

- Share ideas about the habitats of wild animals that live in our neighborhood.

READING STREET ONLINE
CONCEPT TALK VIDEO
www.TexasReadingStreet.com

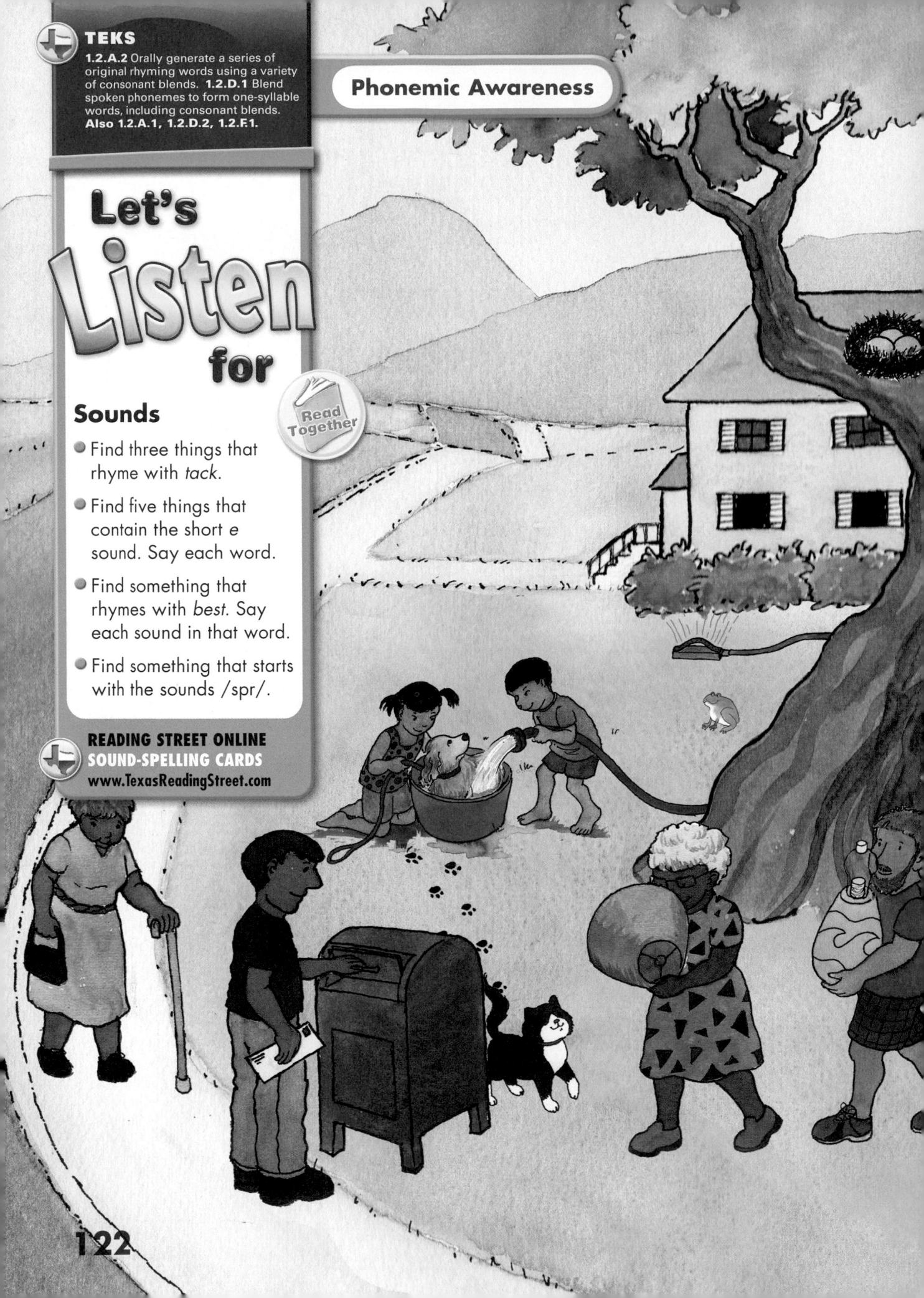

TEKS

1.2.A.2 Orally generate a series of original rhyming words using a variety of consonant blends. **1.2.D.1** Blend spoken phonemes to form one-syllable words, including consonant blends. **Also 1.2.A.1, 1.2.D.2, 1.2.F.1.**

Phonemic Awareness

Let's Listen for

Read Together

Sounds

- Find three things that rhyme with *tack*.

- Find five things that contain the short *e* sound. Say each word.

- Find something that rhymes with *best*. Say each sound in that word.

- Find something that starts with the sounds /spr/.

READING STREET ONLINE
SOUND-SPELLING CARDS
www.TexasReadingStreet.com

123

TEKS

1.3.A Decode words in context and in isolation by applying common letter-sound correspondences, including single letter short e. **1.3.C.1.i** Use common syllabication patterns to decode words, including closed syllable (CVC). **Also 1.3.H.**

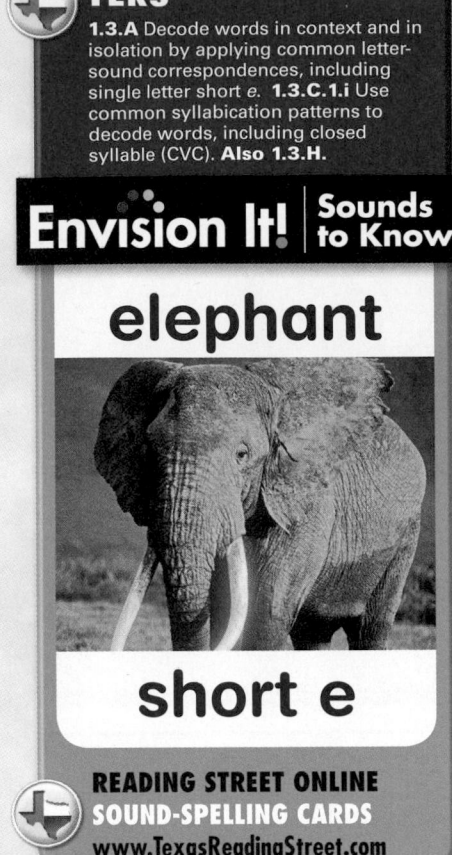

Envision It! | Sounds to Know

elephant

short e

**READING STREET ONLINE
SOUND-SPELLING CARDS**
www.TexasReadingStreet.com

Phonics

🎯 Short *e: e*

Words I Can Blend

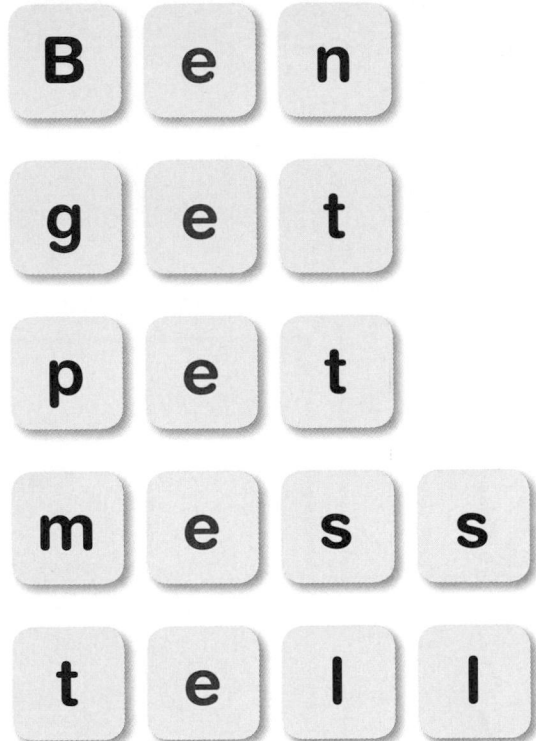

B e n

g e t

p e t

m e s s

t e l l

Sentences I Can Read

1. Ben can get a pet.

2. Tell him to fix his mess.

Words I Can Read

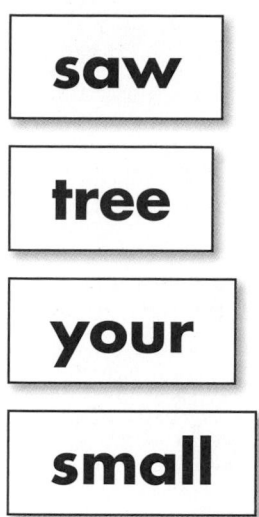

saw

tree

your

small

Sentences I Can Read

1. Nell saw a big nest in the tree.

2. A small pen is on your desk.

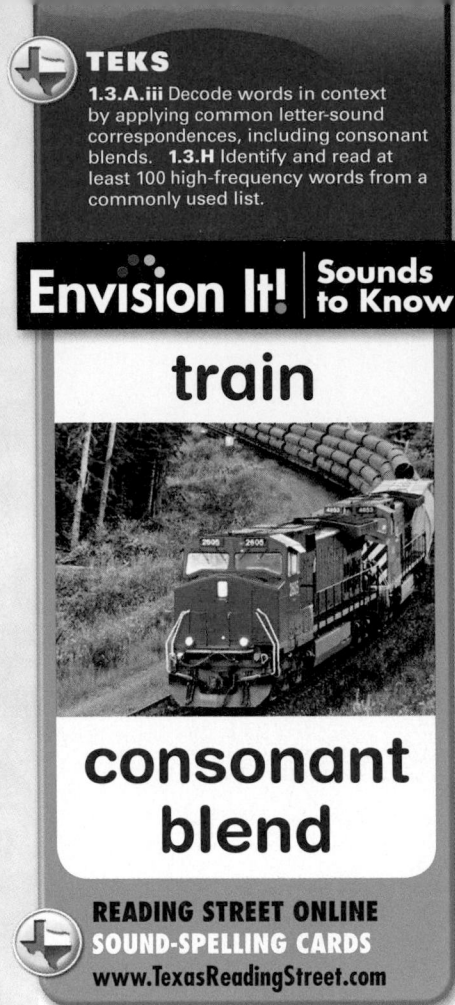
Phonics

Initial Consonant Blends

Words I Can Blend

s t o p

b l a ck

p l a n s

s t e p

g r a s s

Sentences I Can Read

1. Sam will stop and get his black vest.

2. Ned plans to step on grass.

Deb and Spot stop at a small tree.
Drip! Drip! Drip! Deb gets wet.

Deb saw Spot. Spot gets wet.
Deb! Your dress is wet.
"What is it?" asks Deb.

Deb spots a nest. The mom in the nest
lets her kids sip drips from a wet stem.

The drips get Deb and Spot wet.

You've learned

◉ Short e: e
◉ Initial Consonant Blends

High-Frequency Words

saw   tree

your   small

Get the Egg!

by Alyssa Satin Capucilli
illustrated by Bernard Adnet

Genre

Realistic fiction is a made-up story that could really happen. In the next story you will read about a boy and a girl like you.

Question of the Week

Which wild animals live in our neighborhood?

Kim saw Brad at the tree.
A big red bird is in its nest, Kim.

Yes, Brad.
Six eggs sit in the nest.

Snap! A big twig hit the nest!
Snap, snap!
The big twig hit an egg!

Stop the egg, Brad. Stop it!
Can you get it?

The net! Get your net, Brad.
You can help.
Get the egg in your net.

Yes! You did it, Brad.
You can help, Kim.
Set the egg back in its nest.

Brad is at the tree.
The big red bird is back, Kim.

136

Yes, Brad.
It is in its nest.
Six small birds sit in the nest!

TEKS
1.9 Provide evidence from text to support understanding. 1.12.A.1 Read independently for a sustained period of time. Also 1.9.A.2.

138

Think Critically

1. In *Get the Egg!*, Brad and Kim have an adventure. Find and read one part of the story that reminds you of something exciting that has happened to you. Text to Self

2. Why did the author write this story? Author's Purpose

3. What is this story about?
   Main Idea and Details

4. Does this story have a happy ending? Explain.
   Story Structure

5. **Look Back and Write** Look back at pages 134 and 135. Write about how Brad and Kim save the red bird's egg. Provide evidence from the story. Discuss what you wrote with a partner.

TEST PRACTICE Extended Response

Alyssa Satin Capucilli

Alyssa Satin Capucilli writes stories in a notebook she calls her "treasure keeper." Ms. Capucilli once saved a bird that had fallen from its nest. She wrote *Get the Egg!* when she remembered how proud she felt after saving the bird.

Here are other books by Alyssa Satin Capucilli.

Use the Reading Log in the *Reader's and Writer's Notebook* to record your independent reading.

TEKS

1.18.A Write brief stories that include a beginning, middle, and end. **1.21.C.3** Recognize punctuation marks at the end of interrogative sentences. **1.21.C.6** Use punctuation marks at the end of interrogative sentences. **Also 1.21.B.i**

Let's Write It!

Key Features of a Realistic Story

- characters, events, and setting seem real
- characters do things that really can happen

READING STREET ONLINE
GRAMMAR JAMMER
www.TexasReadingStreet.com

Narrative

Realistic Story

A **realistic story** is a made-up story that could happen in real life. The student model on the next page is an example of a realistic story.

Writing Prompt Think about animals in neighborhoods. Write a realistic story about two friends seeing an animal.

Writer's Checklist

Remember, you should . . .

☑ write a story with events that could really happen.

☑ make sure your story has a beginning, a middle, and an end.

☑ make sure any question ends with a question mark.

The Deer

A deer came to the park.
Then Zef and Teresa saw it.
The deer looked hungry.
Zef wanted to leave it six
grapes. His dad said no. Will
they see the deer again?

**Genre
Realistic Story**
This story tells about an event that could really happen.

**Writing Trait
Organization**
The story has a beginning, middle, and end.

This **question** begins with a capital letter and ends with a question mark.

Conventions

- ## Interrogative Sentences

Remember A **question** asks something. It begins with a **capital letter.** It ends with a **question mark (?).**

141

TEKS

1.15.A.1 Follow written multi-step directions with picture cues.

Science in Reading

Genre
How-to Article

- A how-to article is procedural text that tells you how to make or do something.

- A how-to article is usually a set of directions.

- The directions in a how-to article are often numbered. They are listed in the order you should do each step, from first to last.

- If you follow the directions as they are written, you will be successful.

- Read "Help the Birds." As you read, think about what you've learned about how-to articles.

Help the Birds

Birds like to eat.
You can help.

1 Get a small twig.

2 Dip it here.

3 Dip it in this.

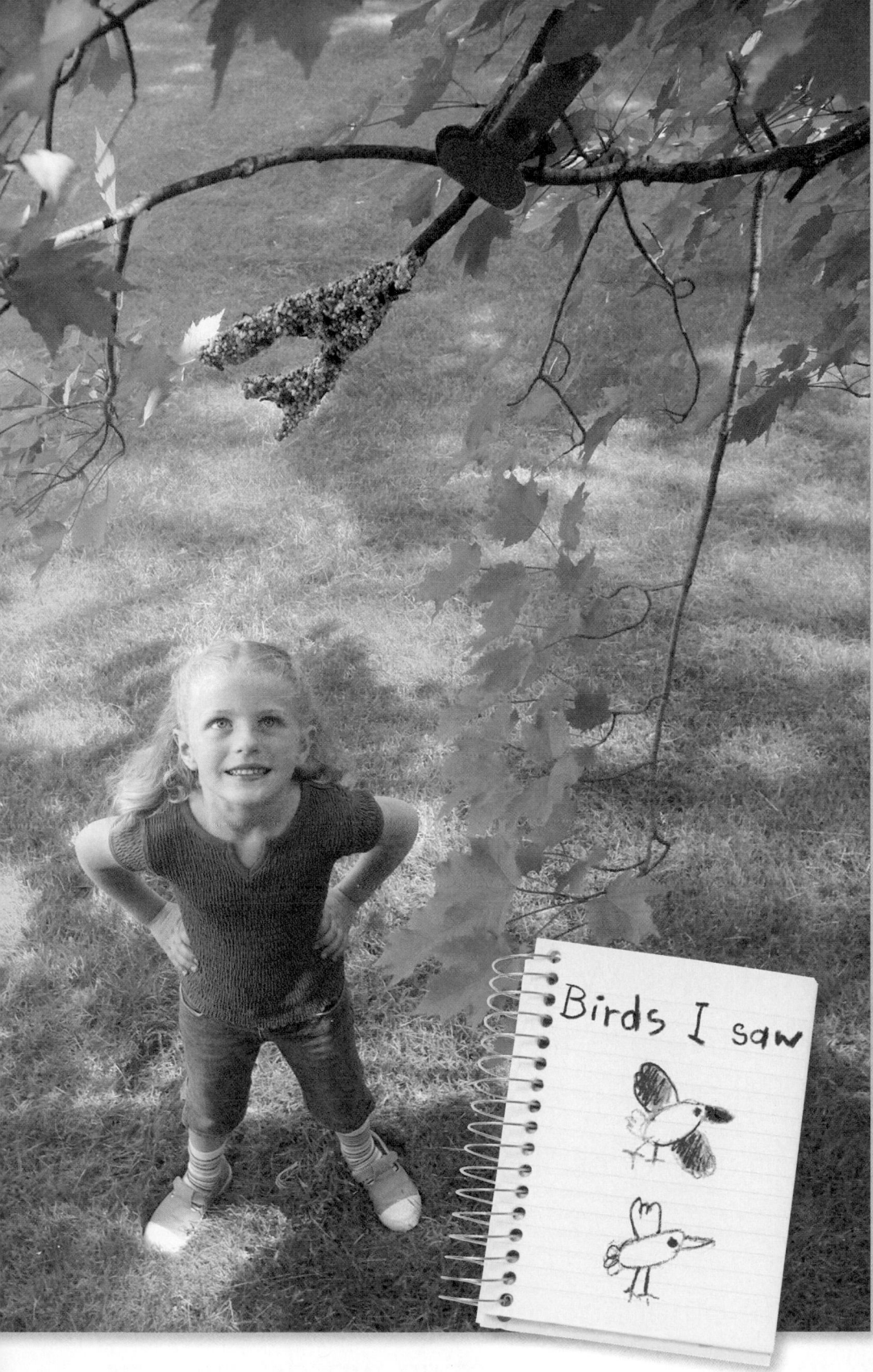

4 Clip it to your tree.
Watch the birds come.

Let's **Think** About...

What might happen if you did not follow the second step?
How-to Article

Let's **Think** About...

Read the directions, following each step. What did you make or do?
How-to Article

Let's **Think** About...

Reading Across Texts How is the girl in "Help the Birds" like Brad and Kim in *Get the Egg!*?

Writing Across Texts If Brad and Kim decided to make treats for the six small birds, what would they make? Write a how-to article for them.

TEKS

1.5.A.1 Read aloud grade-level appropriate text with fluency. **1.5.A.2** Read aloud grade-level appropriate text with comprehension. **1.6.D** Identify and sort words into conceptual categories. **1.20.A.3** Understand and use descriptive adjectives in the context of reading, writing, and speaking. **1.27.A.1** Listen attentively to speakers.

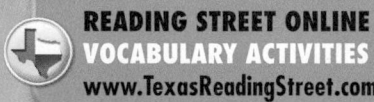

Today was a fun day! We went to a huge park. We played all day. We saw two little rabbits by two tall, green trees.

READING STREET ONLINE
VOCABULARY ACTIVITIES
www.TexasReadingStreet.com

Listening and Speaking

Use descriptive words to make stories more interesting.

Give Descriptions We can use descriptive words, or adjectives, to make a story we tell more interesting. Words such as *fun* and *tall* tell about people, places, things, and events.

Practice It! Tell others about something that happened to you. Use descriptive words, such as *green* and *tall*, to make the story more interesting.

144

Vocabulary

When we **sort words,** we put them into groups that make sense.

cat **dog** **raccoon** **squirrel**

These animals are tame. These animals are wild.

Practice It! Read these words. Sort them into two groups—animals that fly and animals that do not fly.

fox **ox** **bee** **cow** **bird**

Fluency

Appropriate Phrasing When you come to a period, you know it is the end of a sentence. Stop reading at the period.

Practice It!

1. Stop and get your net.

2. Ben, come see the frog by the tree.

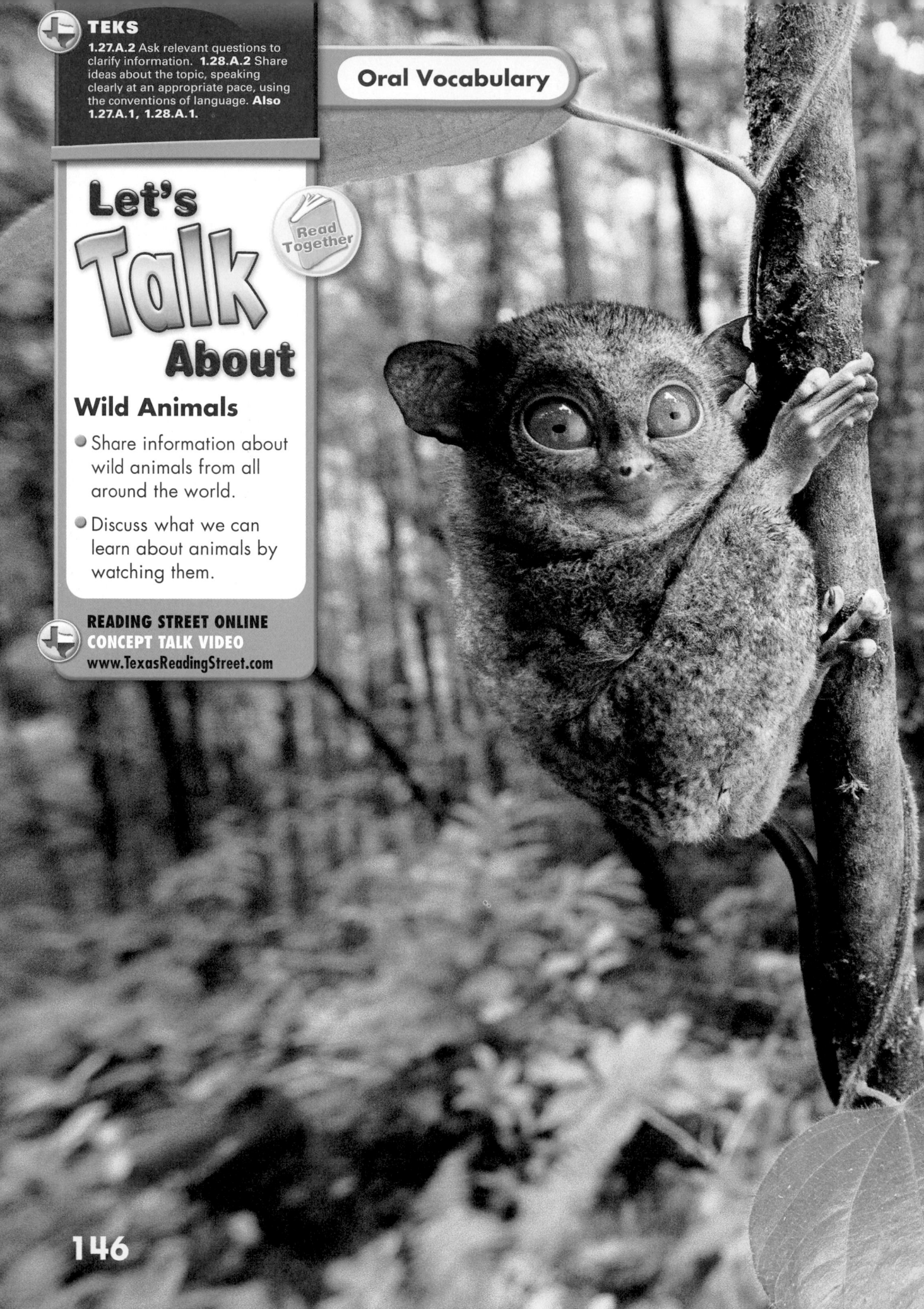

TEKS

1.27.A.2 Ask relevant questions to clarify information. **1.28.A.2** Share ideas about the topic, speaking clearly at an appropriate pace, using the conventions of language. **Also 1.27.A.1, 1.28.A.1.**

Oral Vocabulary

Let's Talk About

Wild Animals

- Share information about wild animals from all around the world.

- Discuss what we can learn about animals by watching them.

READING STREET ONLINE
CONCEPT TALK VIDEO
www.TexasReadingStreet.com

You've learned
0 8 6
Amazing Words
so far this year!

TEKS

1.2.A.2 Orally generate a series of original rhyming words using a variety of consonant blends. **1.2.F.1** Segment spoken one-syllable words of three to five phonemes into individual phonemes.

Phonemic Awareness

Let's Listen for

Read Together

Sounds

- Find two things that rhyme with *trust*.

- Find five things that contain the short *u* sound.

- Find something that rhymes with *dunk*. Say each sound in the word.

READING STREET ONLINE
SOUND-SPELLING CHARTS
www.TexasReadingStreet.com

TEKS

1.3.A Decode words in context and in isolation by applying common letter-sound correspondences, including single letter short *u*. **1.3.C.1.i** Use common syllabication patterns to decode words, including closed syllable (CVC). **Also 1.3.H.**

Envision It! | Sounds to Know

umbrella

short u

READING STREET ONLINE
SOUND-SPELLING CARDS
www.TexasReadingStreet.com

Phonics

Short *u*: *u*

Words I Can Blend

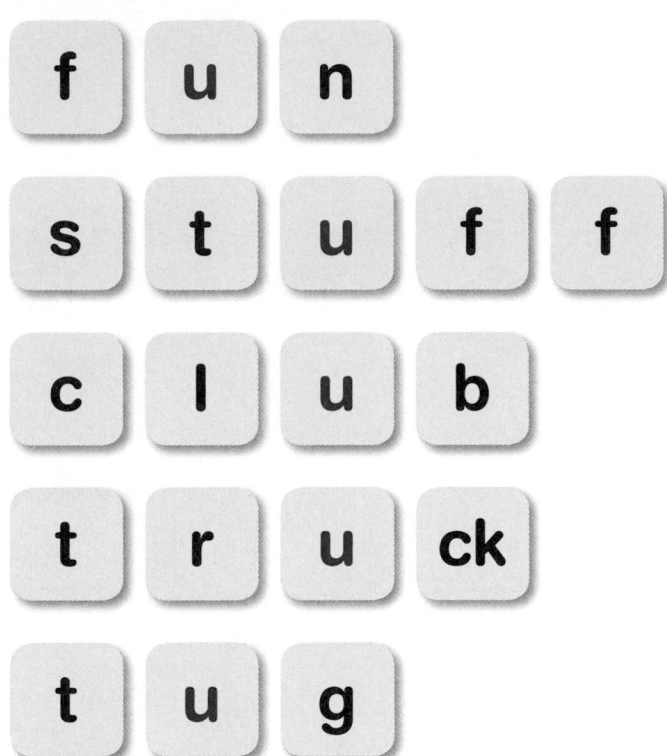

f u n

s t u f f

c l u b

t r u ck

t u g

Sentences I Can Read

1. Ken gets fun stuff in his club.

2. My big truck can tug his little truck.

Words I Can Read

home

many

them

into

Sentences I Can Read

1. Fred has many rugs at home.

2. Tuck them into bed.

TEKS

1.3.A.iii Decode words in context by applying common letter-sound correspondences, including consonant blends. **1.3.H** Identify and read at least 100 high-frequency words from a commonly used list.

Envision It! | **Sounds to Know**

lamp

consonant blend

READING STREET ONLINE
SOUND-SPELLING CARDS
www.TexasReadingStreet.com

Phonics

Final Consonant Blends

Words I Can Blend

j u s t

d e s k

b e s t

t e n t

s a n d

Sentences I Can Read

1. Jess just sat at his desk.

2. Bud set up his best tent on hot sand.

Judd has fun in mud. Will Judd jump in mud? Yes!

And Judd will stand on the rug. Many clumps of mud end up on the rug!

Mom and Dad get home. "Yuck! Get into the tub, Judd."

Judd gets rid of his mud in the tub. Mom and Dad are glad. Judd can help them rub mud from the rug.

You've learned

🔄 Short u: u
🔄 Final Consonant Blends

High-Frequency Words
home   many   them   into

153

Animal Park

by Judy Nayer

Literary nonfiction is about real places and events told like a story. Next you will read about some wild animals in Africa.

Africa

What can we learn about wild animals by watching them?

The hot sun is up at camp.
Camp is in a big, big park.

This land is home to many
animals. Can we see them?
Yes! Just get in the truck.

Bump, bump, bump!
Quick, stop!
A band of zebras runs past us.
They blend into the grass.

Big cats rest up.
They had a big hunt.
Cubs can bat at bugs.

Big birds stand in tan grass.
They can run fast!

Big hippos sit in wet mud.
It is hot, but mud is not hot!

Big elephants stand and sip
in the pond.
They can stomp and swim in it.

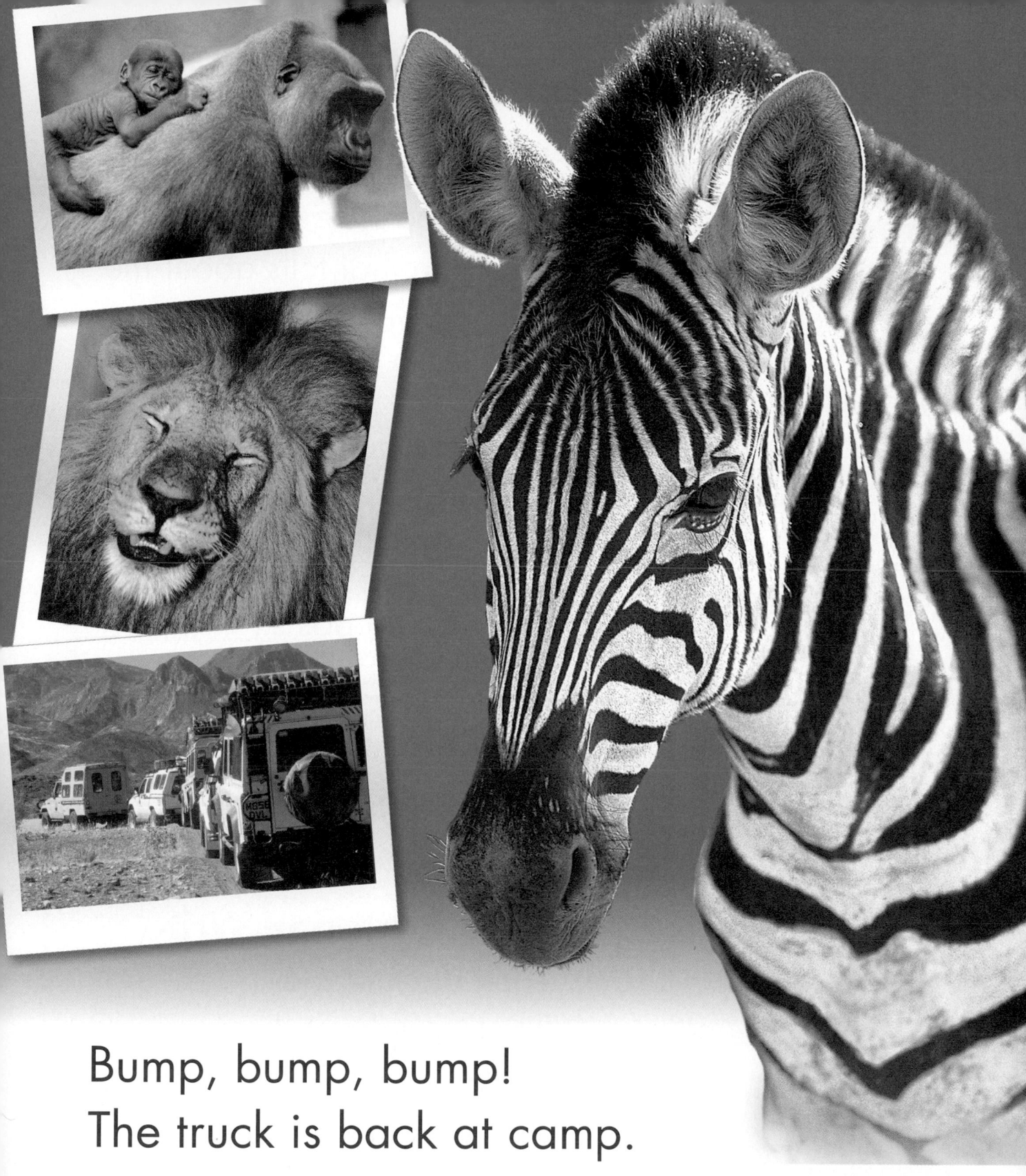

Bump, bump, bump!
The truck is back at camp.

This park is home to many animals.
It was fun to see them!

TEKS

1.10 Provide evidence from text to support understanding. **1.12.A.1** Read independently for a sustained period of time.

Envision It! | **Retell**

READING STREET ONLINE STORY SORT
www.TexasReadingStreet.com

Think Critically

1. **Put yourself in the animal park. Read the part of the selection that tells about the animals you would like to see.** Text to Self

2. **Does the author seem to like animals? Explain why or why not.** Author's Purpose

3. **Why do hippos sit in the mud?** Cause and Effect

4. **Which animals does the author see before the hippos?** Text Structure

5. **Look Back and Write** Look back at the photographs in the selection. Choose an animal that was in the big park. Use facts from the selection to write about the animal you choose.

TEST PRACTICE Extended Response

Judy Nayer

Maybe you have seen big animals in a zoo. Judy Nayer wanted to show you where some of these animals really live, in Africa. Ms. Nayer writes every day. She says, "I often work late at night, when it's very quiet."

Here are other books by Judy Nayer.

Use the Reading Log in the *Reader's and Writer's Notebook* to record your independent reading.

TEKS

1.19.A.1 Write brief compositions about topics of interest to the student. **1.21.C.2** Recognize punctuation marks at the end of exclamatory sentences. **1.21.C.5** Use punctuation marks at the end of exclamatory sentences. **Also 1.20.B.1**

Let's Write It!

Key Features of a Brief Composition

- tells about real people or things
- tells about just one topic

READING STREET ONLINE
GRAMMAR JAMMER
www.TexasReadingStreet.com

Expository

Brief Composition

Compositions tell about real things. The student model on the next page is an example of a brief composition.

Writing Prompt Think about wild animals. Write a composition about what people learn by watching wild animals.

Writer's Checklist

Remember, you should . . .

☑ tell about real wild animals.

☑ make sure each sentence tells one idea.

☑ write an exclamatory sentence at the end, and say the sentence with strong feeling.

Watching Birds

Mom and I see birds in the trees. They are not pets.
We learn about birds.
Birds eat berries.
They live in nests.
Birds eat a lot!

Writing Trait Focus
Sentences should **focus** on the topic.

Genre Brief Composition
This article tells facts about real birds.

This **exclamatory sentence** shows that the writer is surprised.

Conventions

- **Exclamatory Sentences**

- **Remember** An **exclamatory sentence** shows a strong feeling. It ends with an **exclamation mark (!).**

TEKS
1.8.A.1 Respond to rhythm in poetry.
1.8.A.2 Respond to rhyme in poetry.
1.8.A.4 Use rhythm in poetry.
1.8.A.5 Use rhyme in poetry.

Genre
Poetry

- *Poetry* is another word for *poems*. The author of a poem is called a poet.

- A poem tells a story or expresses the poet's feelings about something.

- A poem is written in lines. Often the words at the ends of the lines rhyme.

- A poem usually has a rhythm, or a regular pattern of beats.

- Some poems have alliteration, or words close to each other with the same beginning sound.

- As you read "My Dog Rags," "Raccoon," and "The Hippo," look for elements of poetry.

- Find the alliteration in "My Dog Rags." Which words begin with the same sound?

My Dog Rags

I have a dog and his
name is Rags.

He eats so much that
his tummy sags.

His ears flip-flop
and his tail wig-wags,

And when he walks
he zig-zig-zags!

Raccoon by Betsy Lewin

Raccoons are not a fussy clan
when it comes time to eat.

They'll even raid a garbage can
to find a midnight treat.

The Hippo
by Douglas Florian

By day the hippo loves to float

On swamps and lakes,
much like a boat.

At night from water it retreats,

And eats

   and eats

      and eats

         and eats.

illustrated by
Patrice Aggs

Let's **Think** About...

Point out the words that rhyme in each poem. Clap the rhythm in each poem. **Poetry**

Let's **Think** About...

Reading Across Texts How are the animals in *Animal Park* and the animals in the poems alike? How are they different?

Writing Across Texts Choose any animal, except the hippo, in *Animal Park*. Write a two-line poem about the animal. Use rhythm and words that rhyme at the ends of the lines.

TEKS

1.5.A.1 Read aloud grade-level appropriate text with fluency. **1.5.A.2** Read aloud grade-level appropriate text with comprehension. **1.6.D** Identify and sort words into conceptual categories. **1.20.B.1** Speak in complete sentences with correct subject-verb agreement. **1.27.B.1** Follow oral instructions that involve a short related sequence of actions. **1.27.B.2** Restate oral instructions that involve a short related sequence of actions. **Also 1.27.B.3.**

First, I write the letter. Then I put it in the envelope. After I write the address on the envelope, I add a stamp. Then I...

Let's **Learn** It!

Read Together

READING STREET ONLINE VOCABULARY ACTIVITIES
www.TexasReadingStreet.com

Listening and Speaking

Get Ready For Grade 2

Be a good listener when you follow directions.

Follow, Restate, Give Directions When we follow directions, we use good listening skills. We ask the speaker questions. We repeat the directions to show we understand.

Practice It! Listen to your teacher's directions on how to mail a letter. Restate the directions. Then give new directions to a partner. Use sentences.

Vocabulary

An **antonym** is a word that means the opposite of another word.

big

little

Practice It! Read these words. Write and say an antonym for each word.

fast   in   up   on   back

Fluency

Appropriate Phrasing When you come to a question mark as you read, make your voice go up as if you are asking a question.

Practice It!

1. Can Gus put his frogs into the pond?

2. Where will Bud go to swim?

3. Will the dog run with them at last?

Pets

cat

kitten

gerbil

guinea pig

turtle

hamster

parakeet

goldfish

172

puppy

dog

iguana

rabbit

Farm Animals

chick

hen

rooster

horse

goat

pig

cow

ox

calf

pony

sheep

175

Forest Animals

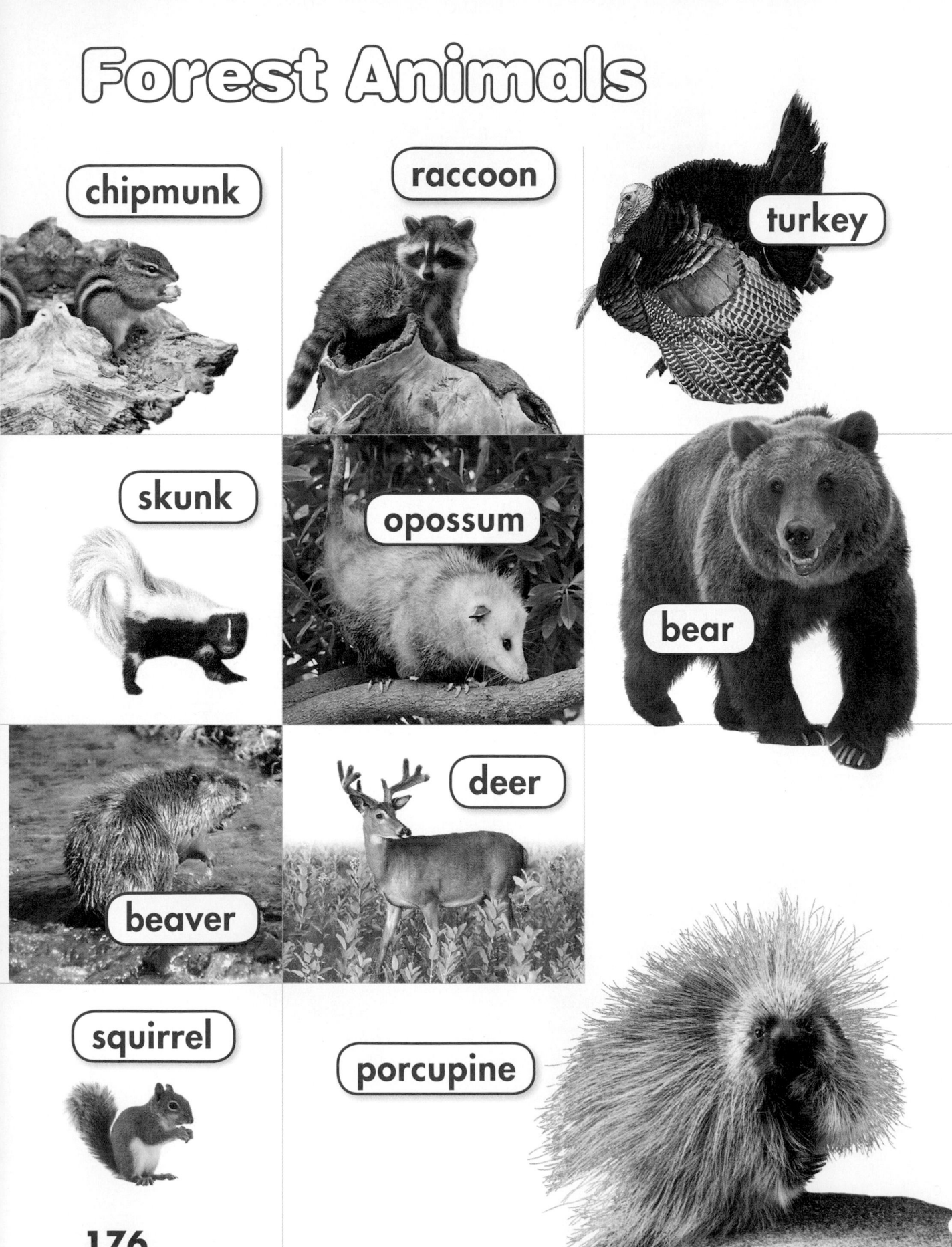

chipmunk

raccoon

turkey

skunk

opossum

bear

beaver

deer

squirrel

porcupine

176

Desert Animals

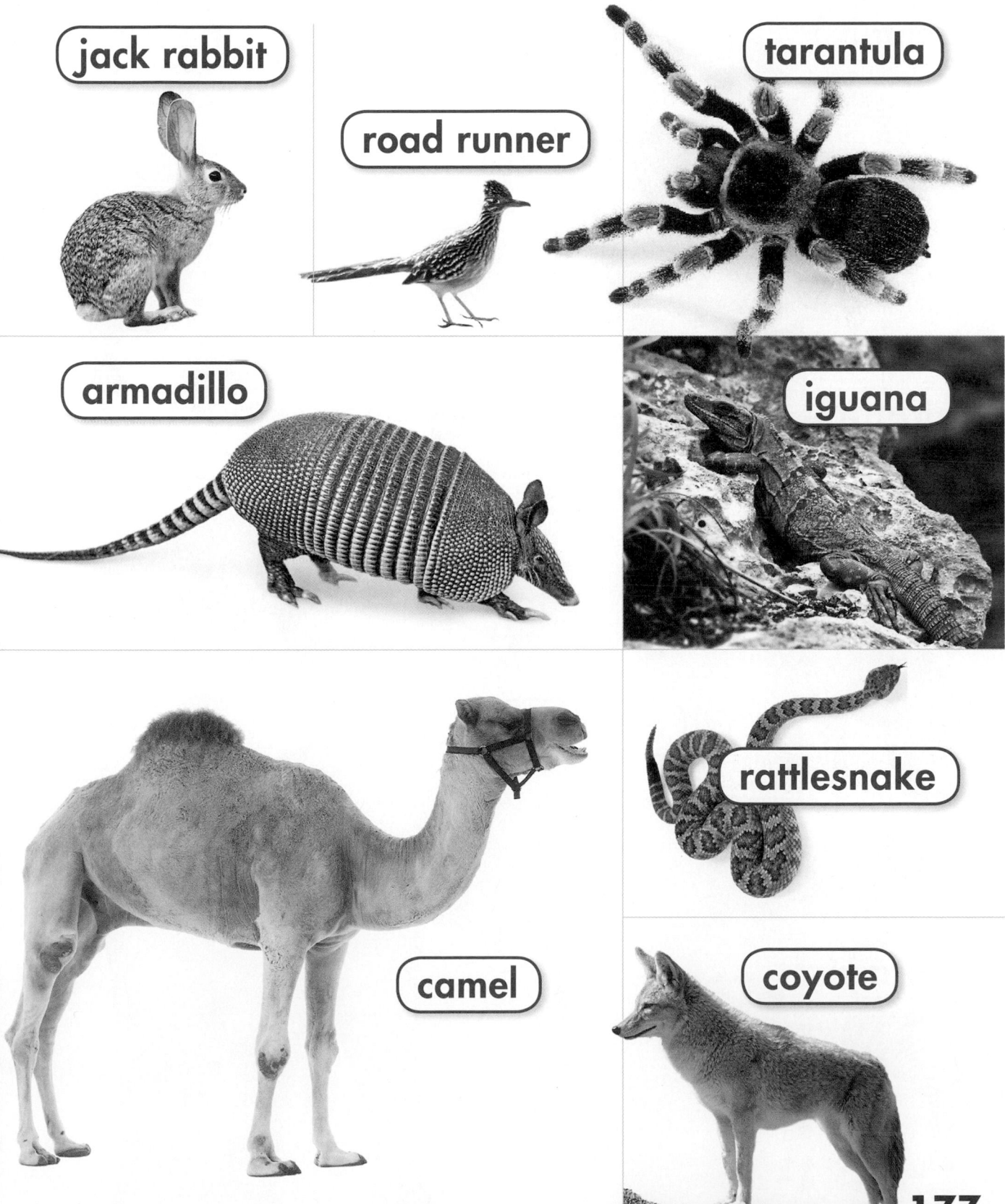

jack rabbit

road runner

tarantula

armadillo

iguana

camel

rattlesnake

coyote

Grassland Animals

cheetah

hyena

rhinoceros

giraffe

anteater

lion

hippopotamus

elephant

zebra

178

Water Animals

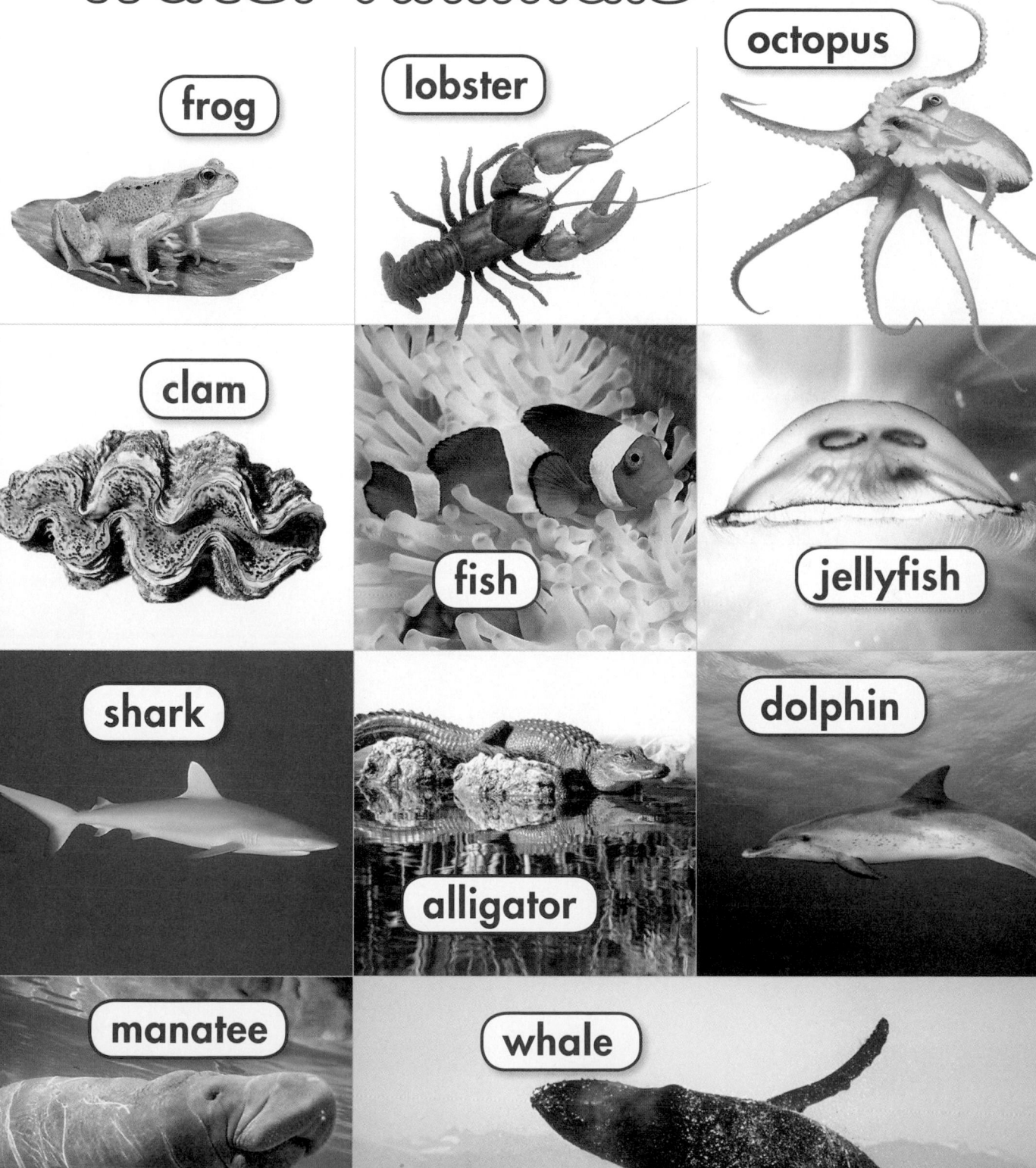

frog

lobster

octopus

clam

fish

jellyfish

shark

alligator

dolphin

manatee

whale

179

Cold-Climate Animals

penguin

lemming

walrus

seal

polar bear

arctic fox

moose

arctic wolf

Underground Animals

mole

meerkat

badger

prairie dog

earthworm

trapdoor spider

Birds

woodpecker

ostrich

goose

robin

crow

cardinal

eagle

duck

owl

hummingbird

pigeon

seagull

Insects and Bugs

ant

caterpillar

beetle

ladybug

cricket

fly

lightning bug

butterfly

spider

grasshopper

bee

Sam, Come Back!

come
in
my
on
way

The Big Blue Ox

blue
from
get
help
little
use

Pig in a Wig

she
take
up
what

A Fox and a Kit

eat
five
four
her
this
too

Animal Park

home
into
many
them

Get the Egg!

saw
small
tree
your

Aa Bb Cc

Dd Ee Ff

Gg Hh Ii

Jj Kk Ll

Mm Nn Oo

Pp Qq Rr

Ss Tt Uu

Vv Ww Xx

Yy Zz

Acknowledgments

Text

Grateful acknowledgment is made to the following for copyrighted material:

Page 168: "Raccoon" from *Animal Snackers* by Betsy Lewin. © 1980, 2004 by Betsy Lewin. Reprinted by permission of Henry Holt and Company, LLC.

Page 169: Excerpt from "The Hippo" in *Mammalabilia*, text copyright © 2000 by Douglas Florian, reprinted by permission of Harcourt, Inc. This material may not be reproduced in any form or by any means without the prior written permission of the publisher.

Note: Every effort has been made to locate the copyright owner of material reproduced on this component. Omissions brought to our attention will be corrected in subsequent editions.

The *Texas Essential Knowledge and Skills for English Language Arts and Reading* reproduced by permission, Texas Education Agency, 1701 N. Congress Avenue, Austin, TX 78701.

Illustrations

Cover Daniel Moreton

14 Robbie Short

20-29, 46-56, 74-83 Janet Stevens

34, 35 Maribel Suarez

40 Marilyn Janovitz

62, 63 Lindsey Gardiner

68 Paul Meisel

98 Ariel Pang

102-111 Charles Santore

116, 117 Jaime Zollars

126 Carol Koeller

128-141 Bernard Adnet

154 Victor Rivas

Photographs

Every effort has been made to secure permission and provide appropriate credit for photographic material. The publisher deeply regrets any omission and pledges to correct errors called to its attention in subsequent editions.

Unless otherwise acknowledged, all photographs are the property of Pearson Education, Inc.

Photo locators denoted as follows: Top (T), Center (C), Bottom (B), Left (L), Right (R), Background (Bkgd)

10 (B) ©Larry Williams/Corbis

36 ©DK Images

38 ©Picture Partners/Alamy Images

65 Getty Images, Joe McDonald/Corbis, Peter Arnold/Getty Images

66 (B) ©Chris Marona/Photo Researchers, Inc.

88 (BL) Getty Images

89 (TL) Mark Richards/PhotoEdit

90 (BR) Peter Olive/Photofusion Picture Library/Alamy Images

91 (TR) A. Ramey/PhotoEdit, (TL) Copyright Bryan & Cherry Alexander Photography/Bryan and Sherry Alexander Photography, (C) Dallas and John Heaton/Corbis

93 Daryl Balfour/Getty Images

94 (B) ©San Diego Zoo/Handout/Reuters/Corbis

118 (TR) Getty Images

121 ©Aristide Economopoulos/Star Ledger/Corbis

145 American Images Inc/Getty Images, Frank Lukasseck/Getty Images, Joel Sartore/Getty Images, Purestock/Getty Images

146 ©Frans Lanting/Corbis

147 ©Heidi & Hans-Jurgen Koch/Minden Pictures

154 (TL) Getty Images, (Bkgd) Tim Davis/Corbis

156 (BR) Craig Lovell/Corbis, (Bkgd) Photo Researchers, Inc.

157 (TR, BR) Digital Stock, (CR) Digital Vision, (L) Staffan Widstrand/Corbis

158 (TC) Jupiter Images, (Bkgd) Tom Nebbia/Corbis

159 (CC) Art Wolfe/Art Wolfe Inc., (TC) Tom Brakefield/Corbis

160 (TC) Beverly Joubert/NGS Image Collection, (BC) Peter Johnson/Corbis

162 (T) ©Theo Allofs/Getty Images

163 (TL) Brand X Pictures, (BL) David Young-Wolff/Alamy Images, (Bkgd) Digital Vision, (CL) Norbert Rosing/NGS Image Collection

171 Mira/Alamy Images, Phil Schermeister/Getty Images.

High-Frequency Words

Identify and read the high-frequency words that you learned in unit R and unit 1.

Unit R.1
a
green
I
see

Unit R.2
like
one
we

Unit R.3
do
look
was
yellow
you

Unit R.4
are
have
that
they
two

Unit R.5
he
is
three
to
with

Unit R.6
for
go
here
me
where

Unit 1.1
come
my
way

Unit 1.2
she
take
up
what

Unit 1.3
blue
from
help
little
use

Unit 1.4
eat
five
four
her

this
too

Unit 1.5
saw
small
tree
your

Unit 1.6
home
into
many
them

Unit 2.1
catch
good
no
put
said
want

Unit 2.2
be
could
horse
of
old
paper

Unit 2.3
live
out
people
who
work

Unit 2.4
down
inside
now
there
together

Unit 2.5
around
find
food
grow
under
water

Unit 2.6
also
family
new
other
some
their

High-Frequency Words

Unit 3.1
always
become
day
everything
nothing
stays
things

Unit 3.2
any
enough
ever
every
own
sure
were

Unit 3.3
away
car
friends
house
our
school
very

Unit 3.4
afraid
again
few
how
read
soon

Unit 3.5
done
know
push
visit
wait

Unit 3.6
before
does
good-bye
oh
right
won't

Unit 4.1
about
enjoy
gives
surprise
worry
would

Unit 4.2
colors
draw
drew
great
over
show
sign

Unit 4.3
found

mouth
once
took
wild

Unit 4.4
above
eight
laugh
moon
touch

Unit 4.5
picture
remember
room
stood
thought

Unit 4.6
across
because
dance
only
opened
shoes
told

Unit 5.1
along
behind
eyes
never
pulling

toward

Unit 5.2
door
loved
should
wood

Unit 5.3
among
another
instead
none

Unit 5.4
against
goes
heavy
kinds
today

Unit 5.5
built
early
learn
science
through

Unit 5.6
answered
carry
different
poor